Trust Be

Munchausen synd. ~~ome by proxy,~~ inter-agency child protection and partnership with families

Edited by Jan Horwath and Brian Lawson

Acknowledgements

We are indebted to many people who have helped us and shown a great deal of grace under the pressure of putting on the conference and in assisting in the production of this book.

Thanks are due in particular to Richard White, Terence Stephenson, Sandra Shaw, D.I. John Fox, staff from the now defunct Child Abuse Training Unit and Alison Love from the National Children's Bureau press office whose support was crucial in making the conference a success.

Our administrative support has also been vital and we would like to thank Rachel Brown, Zoe Buxton, Christine Chu, Angela Elliott, Frankie Froggatt, Jayne Laycock, Lynne Tyler and Donna Wallace without whom there would have been no conference and no book.

Our thanks are also due to members of Wakefield Area Child Protection Committee in particular Val Barker, Mike Baxter, Ernest Dews and Jenny Smith for their support in helping to put on a major conference which some felt would not be possible.

We would also like to acknowledge our debt to Professor Meadow, without whose work this issue may well still be undetected.

Finally we are indebted to those practitioners and trainers in the north of England who were prepared to share with us their experiences and knowledge with regard to Munchausen syndrome by proxy, the results of which were the first national conference held in October 1994 and this publication.

Contents

List of tables

List of figures

List of contributors

Martin Banks
Is a manager of four child protection investigation teams in Staffordshire and has contributed to the development of the practice of covert video surveillance. He qualified as a social worker in 1979. Since then he has worked predominantly within statutory child care agencies, both as a social worker and as a guardian ad litem.

Arnon Bentovim MBBS FRC Psych DPH
Is honorary senior lecturer to the Behavioural Science Unit of the Institute of Child Health and consultant to Great Ormond Street Hospital for Children and the Tavistock Clinic. From 1968 – 1994 he was consultant child psychiatrist of Great Ormond Street and at the Tavistock Clinic from 1975 – 1994. In this capacity he was responsible for child protection and founded the sexual abuse and treatment team and the child care consultation services.

John Fox
Is a detective inspector for Hampshire Police Authority, having worked for the police for 20 years. He has been involved in child protection investigations for the last three years including suspected cases of MSBP.

Jenny Gray
Is the former team manager at the social work department at Great Ormond Street Hospital for Children. She has a social work background but also has a Diploma in family therapy and a Diploma in teaching and course design in higher education.

Jan Horwath
Is lecturer in the Department of Sociological Studies at Sheffield University and manager for a team of child care and child protection trainers for Sheffield Family and Community Services. She has a social work background having worked in juvenile justice,

probation and child protection settings. Her research interests include evaluating the quality and outcomes of training, user involvement in training and she is also researching the effectiveness of child protection systems and child care professionals as abusers.

Norma Howes
Is an independent social worker, therapist, consultant and trainer specialising in work with abused children and adults. She previously worked in a specialist child protection team and has a major interest in the links between trauma and dissociation.

Margaret Kessel
Is a senior social worker at the Children's Hospital in Sheffield. She has extensive experience of paediatric social work, focusing particularly on child protection. As a practitioner she has been involved with a number of alleged and proven cases of MSBP.

Brian Lawson
Is the multi-agency child protection trainer for Sheffield Area Child Protection Committee. He has a social work background and has worked in a number of joint child care and mental health projects as well as in child protection.

Anna Markowycz
Is a member of the Humberside Panel of Guardians ad litem. She serves on both local and national multi-disciplinary committees regarding policy development and training in relation to child witnesses. She was previously a court welfare officer in the probation service. Anna has acted as guardian ad litem for a number of children where allegations of MSBP abuse have been the focus of the proceedings.

Chris Middleton
Is a senior lecturer at Mid-Trent College of Nursing and Midwifery, teaching child protection. He is editor of the Newsletter for the Royal College of Nursing Child Protection Special Interest Group and is chair of the East Midlands branch of BASPCAN. He has a nursing background working in surgery, accident and emergency, burns and plastics as a children's and general nurse.

Peter Milla Msc MBBS FRCP
Is reader in Paediatric Gastroenterology at the Institute of Child Health at Great Ormond Street Hospital for Children.

Barbara Miller
Is a probation officer in Lincolnshire and has experience of work-

ing with offenders suffering from MSBP. Barbara joined the probation service in 1988.

Paul Miller

Is an assistant chief probation officer in Lincolnshire and has functional responsibility for work with mentally disordered offenders. He joined the probation service in 1978 and throughout his career has maintained an interest in mental health.

Dr Colin Morley

Is employed by the University of Cambridge as a lecturer in paediatrics and works as an honorary consultant paediatrician at Addenbrookes Hospital, Cambridge. He is the senior consultant in the Neonatal Intensive Care Unit, specialising in neonatal respiratory problems. In addition he is the senior paediatrician for a general paediatric 'firm' where he has a particular interest in infants and children with respiratory problems and apnoiec attacks. He is also the paediatric representative on the Cambridgeshire Area Child Protection Committee and has experience of cases of child protection and MSBP. His research interests and publications are on respiratory problems and sudden infant death syndrome.

Gretchen Precey

Gretchen Precey has been a senior practitioner at the Clermont Child Protection Unit in Brighton since 1992. Prior to that she worked as a senior practitioner for Norfolk Social Services' Children and Families and also in Yorkshire in the field of child and adolescent psychiatry and child guidance. Her main area of interest and expertise is the interviewing and treatment of children who have been sexually abused. She has presented training courses on interviewing techniques and direct work with children both in East Sussex and nationally.

Sandra Shaw

Is operations director for Children and Family Services in Staffordshire Social Services Department and has overall responsibility for services provided to children and families within Staffordshire. The range of services include day nurseries, children's homes, family placements, child protection services, youth justice and social work help to children and families. She has a social work background, and has a Master of Science degree in public sector management.

Terence Stephenson

Is a senior lecturer in the Department of Child Health at the University of Nottingham and honorary consultant paediatrician at the University Hospital Nottingham and the City Hospital Nottingham. He is a Member of the Royal College of Physicians of the United Kingdom. He works as a general paediatrician and has a particular interest in child protection including MSBP. He has acted as an expert witness in a number of cases of MSBP.

Foreword

Justice Singer, The Royal Courts of Justice, London

At birth we each need to establish secure bonds with our primary carers. A main ingredient of all primary care is trust. Initially it is instinctive and biological on the part of the infant, for whom there is no practical alternative. With the advent of growing mobility, vocal ability and increasing understanding, some elements of choice show the beginnings of the path to self-determination and ultimate independence.

Trust in parental benevolence should be the birthright of every infant. The child should also be able to trust other carers encountered during childhood: the grandparents, uncles, aunts and other members of the immediate family; the child-minder and the baby-sitter; the nursery school worker and teachers; the doctor and the nurse; perhaps also the step-parents or the person or persons with the status of such; maybe the social worker, the foster parents or the prospective adopters.

Part of growing up is the development of an increasingly complex and subtle network of social relationships. Many will depend, if they are to be beneficial, upon trust. Is it simplistic to theorise that there is a direct correlation between the degree of harm wrought by trust's betrayal and the proximity of the betrayer? At that hub, for both infant and child, is the parent or other primary carer: if they betray trust then how often does it seem there is a long-term impact on the child's development?

Trust can also be betrayed in relation to that part of parental responsibility that should procure appropriate health care. Those by and for whom these chapters have been written now acknowledge (though as yet with no precision of definition) as a recognisable pattern of abuse that which we variously describe as Munchausen syndrome by proxy (MSBP), factitious or induced illness, or illness induction syndrome. As with the early dissemination of the shocking concept of physical abuse and sexual abuse, so too has there been disbelief that such a pattern of dysfunctional behaviour can really exist. Yet, rare though it may be by comparison with other more 'conventional' forms of abuse, there are probably few who would now discount it entirely.

Many of the chapters which follow emphasise the importance of vigilance, of accepting MSBP (or more importantly its consequences for the child) as a valid component of differential diagnosis for both health and social workers, and the necessity for developing strategies for appropriate intervention. All these desirable factors must, however, always be balanced by a proper element of caution. Caution that considers all possible alternative causes; caution that will not come to a conclusion without investigating and assessing the relevant child, sibling and parental social and medical history; and caution that shares responsibility among a team structured to enable the requisite specialist and experienced input to be shared, measured and weighed.

Any assessment of MSBP must take into account that until the necessary degree of clarity can be obtained, to broadcast suspicion would not be helpful to a child whose deviant carer might escalate harm in response to declared suspicion.

There are those who see this as a breach of the principle of partnership and who express concern about the element of deceit (or lack of frankness) this may involve. It would be wrong to minimise such ethical considerations. But are they so very different in quality to the current initial decision-making in child protection, when the paediatrician has concluded this is a non-accidental injury and the plans for the immediate protection of the child are being made, which may include considering removal under an emergency protections order? On occasion the parent is not kept informed about the plans if it is felt it would place the child at risk of further abuse. What may be difficult is the duration of the fact-gathering and conclusion-forming period. The lapse of time itself is often an inevitable consequence of exaggeration, lies, manipulative behaviour and other methods of dis-information and camouflage which the suspected perpetrator of MSBP may have employed in the past and may continue to rely upon. Such behaviour is of itself not redolent of the concept of partnership: for examples see among the various case histories described in this volume.

What therefore should emerge as the cardinal and guiding principle is the precept of the child's best interest: and that is as it should be.

The variety of stimuli which tempt or drive adults to injure children or to cause the medical profession to subject them to unnecessary medical treatment is as yet imperfectly understood. The cause is less important than the harm done, but the cause may be critical when it comes to prognosis, and in particular to assessing the risk of rehabilitation. Here again the guiding principle must be the child's best interests. If all those involved can strive to put those interests first they will be fulfilling their professional function.

I commend this volume for the insight it gives into the difficulties faced, by those from the variety of disciplines here represented, when they are required to exercise that responsibility in a case of suspected MSBP.

Introduction

Brian Lawson, Multi-agency Child Protection Trainer, Sheffield

Jan Horwath, Child Care Training Manager and Lecturer, University of Sheffield

Aims and background

This book is concerned with Munchausen Syndrome by Proxy (MSBP) abuse from a viewpoint which, in line with the Children Act 1989, sees the child's welfare as the paramount concern. The book is aimed at practitioners and managers from all disciplines, who may have to face the consequences of dealing with the possibility of a child suffering significant harm as a result of this form of abuse.

MSBP abuse raises issues that are much wider than the narrow focus of child protection. Equally, MSBP acts as a lens through which the essence of some of the greatest dilemmas in current child protection practice are brought into sharp focus. These issues and dilemmas are outlined later in the book. It is our hope that by focusing this book on the welfare of the child and by targeting practitioners from all agencies as its audience, this collection of chapters will have an impact on practice. We seek to promote the following practice principles:

- that investigations and assessments of MSBP abuse should be undertaken within a formal inter-agency child protection framework to agreed principles, processes and procedures;
- that rigorous information gathering and careful assessment, particularly of the wider social context of parent/child interactions and previous history and contact, is needed at all stages prior to decision making;
- that those involved with the family should be clear about their role and responsibility and should hold to these boundaries. There should be a clear task if a professional is to remain involved with the family.

The importance of this approach is emphasised in Chapter 11 by Gray, Bentovim and Milla:

> 'The children's outcomes were not related to the type of severity of the illness induced in them, but to the way in which their cases had been managed.'

MSBP abuse is a small problem in terms of numbers of children who are abused, as Stephenson demonstrates in his overview (Chapter 1), but the impact on the children affected is great and often lethal. As Bools and others (1993) have shown, the outcomes for the children who survive are not encouraging and this is echoed in Chapter 13 on work with survivors. Likewise, any professional involved in a suspected case of MSBP is unlikely to forget the experience. It is our hope that this book will have an impact on practice by raising practitioners' awareness, equipping them to deal with their concerns sensitively and make appropriate assessments so that children are protected without too many families suffering the trauma of unfounded allegations.

In order to achieve these aims, we have taken a facilitative view of our editorial task. We have sought to work with our contributors to assist them to say what they wanted to say. Often this has been a mutually challenging and arduous task as people have been involved in conceptualising and processing difficult and painful experiences.

A prime purpose of this book is to provide practitioners and managers new to MSBP with material to understand what they are facing. We have therefore encouraged descriptions of case material to provide a broad range of experiences from different professional perspectives. Readers more familiar with the issues may decide to pass over some of this detail.

The depth of the case material contributors have been able to provide has depended on a number of factors: the current legal status of the case in question; the permission of relevant parties to have material included; and how individuals draw their own confidentiality boundaries. This material has often been provided after lengthy negotiations with the relevant parties and we are grateful to the contributors for ensuring its release and for sharing their work with us.

We decided to call this book *Trust Betrayed?* because it encapsulates for us the issues faced by professionals and families involved in suspected cases of MSBP. Is the carer betraying the trust placed in them by their child, in order to meet their own needs for attention from medical personnel? Are doctors betraying the trust placed in them by their patient if they subject the child too readily to invasive and unnecessary medical procedures? Or if they make an early assessment of MSBP, are they depriving a child of necessary medical treatment?

This book had its origins in requests from child protection coordinators, medical personnel and trainers to the Child Abuse Training Unit (North) of the National Children's Bureau, for information and guidance on managing suspected cases of MSBP. These requests resulted in the first national conference on MSBP held in conjunction with Wakefield Area Child Protection Committee (ACPC) in October 1994. As organisers of the conference, we were made aware of a national need for guidance in assessing these cases. The conference was oversubscribed and many professionals requested information shared at the conference. We felt a collection of the conference proceedings would not reflect the need for a comprehensive overview. As a result of this we decided to edit a book which, while using contributors to the conference among the authors, would offer an opportunity to examine MSBP in a broader context of child protection and *Working Together under the Children Act 1989* guidelines. We particularly wished to focus on the issues involved in working in partnership with families and professionals in suspected cases of MSBP, dealing with the inevitable dilemmas between action and reluctance to act faced by those working with suspected cases of MSBP. We explore the likely personal and professional challenges practitioners and managers will have to manage in order to respond appropriately to concerns of MSBP abuse.

We also decided to try not to go over in any detail issues that are covered elsewhere. To this end, we recommend that the book be read in conjunction with the work published by Meadow which is extensively referenced in this collection and with Schreier and Libow's *Hurting for Love* (1993). Those with a particular interest in the wider area of factitious illness are referred to Feldman (1994).

Definition of MSBP abuse

Child abuse has been recognised as a 'weak signifier' (Thorpe, 1994) which is socially constructed and historically dependent. The confusion between MSBP as a mental health condition and as a pattern of abusive behaviour formally recognised as a category of abuse to children (see *Working Together* para 6.40) adds to the problem of definition, as does the search for a more appropriate description such as 'induced illness'. Terence Stephenson explores these issues in more detail in the following chapter. This debate is echoed by other contributors throughout the book.

For the purpose of this collection, however, the definition of MSBP abuse is:

> Significant harm which is caused to a child by the actions of a parent or other carer who deliberately fabricate symptoms or induce medical symptoms in a child which would not otherwise be present.
>
> The actions may be as a result of omission or commission and include such behaviours as:

- deliberate poisoning;
- deliberate burning or other damage to the skin to induce symptoms;
- deliberate suffocation to induce symptoms;
- removal of or tampering with necessary equipment;
- introducing foreign material to tests or other behaviour which causes damaging and unnecessary tests to be performed on the child;
- deliberately inducing fits in the child.

An overview of the book

The book is ordered into a broadly chronological sequence. General issues of concern with regard to recognition and assessment are followed by more specific concerns with regard to investigations and court processes; treatment issues are discussed in the final few chapters.

In the first chapter Terence Stephenson places MSBP into a child protection context, looking at recognition, incidence, definition and history. In Chapter 2, Gretchen Precey provides a first-hand account of both the professional issues and the personal impact of dealing with MSBP abuse for the first time.

In Chapter 3, Colin Morley provides his critique of current practice in the assessment of MSBP, in particular highlighting his concerns about MSBP diagnosis and the use of covert video surveillance (CVS) in assessing MSBP.

Chris Middleton writes in Chapter 4 about practice dilemmas faced by nurses in both community and hospital settings. In addition, he examines the controversy surrounding the actions of nurse Beverley Allitt in terms of her status as an alleged MSBP perpetrator. He also examines the recommendations made by the Clothier Inquiry and assesses the likely impact of these on the nursing profession, together with the issues raised by their implementation.

Jan Horwath and Margaret Kessel discuss further the dilemmas raised in dealing with potential cases of MSBP abuse, focusing on issues of professional dangerousness and its impact on risk assessment in potential cases of MSBP (Chapter 5).

Issues surrounding the use of CVS are considered in detail in two chapters: Sandra Shaw describes an Area Child Protection Committee management protocol developed in Staffordshire (Chapter 6); while Martin Banks considers practice issues (Chapter 7).

Detective Inspector John Fox takes a child-centred view of the necessity of criminal investigation in Chapter 8 and illustrates his argument with case material. He argues strongly for covert video surveillance to be undertaken by the police as a formal investigative procedure and suggests this as part of a protocol for investigating MSBP. He also pays particular attention to the role of expert witnesses in such cases. Anna Markowycz takes a family court-based view of MSBP in Chapter 9, focusing on the balancing acts in which the courts became involved when making judgements based on conflicting material from carers and doctors. She also provides some information on relevant case law and guidance and examines how best the courts can secure the welfare of the child. In Chapter 10, Terence Stephenson discusses how witnesses should prepare themselves to give evidence in court with regard to MSBP.

Jenny Gray, Arnon Bentovim and Peter Milla provide valuable information in Chapter 11 on both treatment for perpetrators and prognosis for rehabilitation based on research of their experience of working with MSBP abuse at Great Ormond Street Hospital for Children. Barbara Miller and Paul Miller from Lincolnshire Probation Service look at the roles of the probation service in relation to MSBP and the contribution they can make both with regard to convicted perpetrators and to our understanding of their seductive grooming processes and dangerousness (Chapter 12).

Developing the focus on therapy, we are pleased to be able to include a chapter by Norma Howes on the impact on adult survivors of MSPB abuse and the therapeutic issues raised for helping such survivors (Chapter 13). During the course of writing this book we have been in touch with a number of therapists working in relative isolation with MSBP survivors as adults and we hope this will be of assistance and interest both to them and more widely.

Chapter 14 looks at the issues for training in terms of raising agency awareness and promoting high standards of inter-agency practice. We explore the likely training needs for dealing with MSBP abuse and possible ways of meeting them in a variety of different formats. The importance of developing a strategy coordinated by the local Area Child Protection Committee (ACPC) is emphasised and some suggestions are made with regard to possible exercises for training programmes.

We bring all these themes together in the conclusion and look in more detail at the challenges to current practice, how practice might develop and issues that would merit further exploration. We provide some suggestions about redefining our basis of trust so that children can be more adequately protected by safer institutional environments. We feel that this assists in providing us with a basis for maintaining trusting relationships in both our professional and personal lives. We conclude by returning to the debate on the use of the term Munchausen syndrome by proxy.

As we indicated previously, MSBP touches on wider child protection issues as well as those outside the sphere of child protection. In the following sections we highlight these concerns and indicate where these issues are addressed by our contributors.

Specific child protection dilemmas raised by MSBP abuse

The possibility of MSBP abuse brings into sharp focus issues concerned with:

- the challenges to partnership with carers in child protection work;
- drift in the legal system;
- sexual abuse.

The challenges to partnership with carers in child protection work

The principles of partnership and of maximising family participation in child protection work are now established as mainstream practice. This development stems from the philosophy of service provision which underpins the Children Act, the framework for practice established by *Working Together under the Children Act*, and the detailed Guidance, mainly directed at social work practice, recently published by the Department of Health (1995).

These developments have arisen from a combination of messages from two main sources. The first source is a critique on family exclusion in terms of civil rights and the negative impact of this on families falsely accused. This was highlighted by experiences in Cleveland and taken up by parents' groups such as Parents Against Injustice (PAIN).

The second source is work done previously by the Family Rights

Group (1992) and the University of East Anglia (Thorborn and others, 1995) on the possible benefits of carers' (and sometimes children's) direct involvement in the child protection process.

Recently, concerns have been expressed about the way this philosophy is being put into practice. For example, in its report for 1992/93 the Children Act Advisory Committee showed concern with regard to workers' 'exhausting partnership' prior to intervening in order to promote the paramount welfare of the child:

> 'Prima facie if 'reasonable parental care' is lacking the child or the child is beyond control leading to a risk of significant harm to the child, **either** someone else must be shown as able to supply it **or** the Local Authority should have that task.' (their emphasis)

A lack of clarity about when to use authority to intervene in child protection work because of confusion about the meaning of partnership, can feed directly into the kinds of dangerous practice described by Horwath and Kessel in Chapter 5, particularly in terms of denial, collusion and minimisation by workers. Families can also pay lip service to partnership.

Recognition is growing that, in child protection work, practitioners are directly faced with dealing with the central dilemma inherent in the Children Act: that of promoting the paramount welfare of the child whilst at the same time maximising the involvement of carers in that process, carers who may be responsible for significantly harming the child. This is a difficult balance to strike. Indeed at certain stages in the process it may not be possible or even desirable. As the Department of Health Guidance *The Challenge of Partnership in Child Protection* states under the heading 'enquiries and investigation':

> Adults who may be suffering from Munchausen syndrome by proxy or Meadows syndrome should not be consulted or involved at this time. Such is their deviousness that it is dangerous for professionals to make their concerns explicit before they have sufficient evidence to ensure the adequate protection of the child. It is important for the agencies with statutory responsibilities to seek expert advice before they invite such family members to engage in decision making or any level of partnership.

John Fox expresses concern that early confrontation of parents by medical staff, prior to a strategy meeting with the investigating agencies (which excludes the parents under *Working Together* guidelines), can result in a loss of evidence necessary to protect the child in either the civil or criminal courts (Chapter 8).

In order to promote the paramount welfare of the child, guidance does allow for the exclusion of parents from critical parts of the process. The Department of Health is explicit that this should be in exceptional circumstances. As both Martin Banks (Chapter 7) and Sandra Shaw (Chapter 6) state, this includes support for covert video surveillance in certain circumstances.

Our concern is that a focus on 'partnership with parents' can lead workers to lose focus on the child. We would prefer to see the phrase 'working collaboratively for children' used more widely, as advocated by the Pen Green Family Centre in Corby.

As Gray, Bentovim and Milla show in Chapter 11, when the reason for working with adults is focused directly on the needs of the child, this promotes high quality child protection work; for example, when deciding about the rehabilitation of children. Their chapter demonstrates how good partnership work can be undertaken and promoted in this difficult and challenging area of practice. Anna Markowycz's chapter indicates that partnerships with parents in the form of creative and flexible use of section 8 orders are often the preferred options for disposals by the courts where it is deemed that such arrangements will be safe for the child.

Drift in the legal system

The Children Act Advisory Committee Annual Report for 1992/93 expressed concern with regard to the use of expert witnesses. This is amplified in the 1993/94 report and given as one of the prime causes of the failure of Children Act processes to sustain the reduction of delay in the civil courts:

> 'Wide use of experts may lead to children being examined more than is necessary with a resulting increase in distress. There tends also to be more difficulty in achieving an early hearing for long trials particularly where the availability of a number of expert witnesses has to be taken into account . . . As noted last year, where there is a limited number of appropriate experts available that fact also contributes to delay and places particular demands on the individuals themselves in meeting their professional responsibilities.' (p. 13)

The report then goes on to outline and endorse best practice in using expert witnesses in court and also approves of the proposal to develop the concept of the 'appropriate expert' as recommended by an expert witness group.

Cases of MSBP abuse routinely require more than one expert paediatric witness, and it is not unusual for three to be required, in addition to other expert witnesses. These issues are examined in more detail in Terence Stephenson's second paper (Chapter 10) and by Anna Markowycz (Chapter 9).

Sexual abuse and MSBP

As Meadow (1994) states:

'Different authorities include different aspects of parental behaviour in the spectrum of MSBP abuse. Most exclude the false accusations of sexual abuse that partners may make against each other at the time of marriage break-up and during custody disputes. Nevertheless, at times, false accusations of sexual abuse (and physical abuse) do fit firmly into MSBP spectrum. Families are recorded in which the mother has made elaborate accusations of sexual abuse by someone outside the family, and has coached the child to provide impressive disclosure detail, as well as injuring the child to fabricate the signs of sexual abuse. Some of the children and their siblings have also suffered factitious illness. For these children, the false sexual abuse is just one of several false illness/health allegations.' (p. 113)

The wider debate

MSBP abuse of children touches on, and has been brought into, debates much wider than the welfare of children. These include topics such as:

- diagnosis and mental health;
- adult civil liberties;
- sexism;
- safe environments.

Diagnosis and mental health

MSBP has been fiercely debated as a mental health and medical issue (for example, the editorial in *The Lancet* 4 June 1994). Stephenson outlines some of the criteria used for diagnosis of MSBP in an adult in his overview (Chapter 1). The word 'syndrome' implies a condition with an overtone of genetic inevitability, which is fiercely resisted by some. Yet some of the causal explanations (see for example, Schreier and Libow, 1993) imply a deep-seated motivational pathology and this is often reflected in treatment-based disposals of convicted perpetrators. The issue of diagnosis of a mother as having or not having MSBP and the relative importance of this in relation to her children suffering significant harm is often fiercely contested in the civil court.

Some leaders in the field have accepted the problems imposed by the terminology and have moved away from the term 'MSBP abuse' toward 'factitious illness'. Such a move is endorsed by Colin Morley in Chapter 3. Gretchen Precey discusses some of the issues in Chapter 2 and Gray, Bentovim and Milla refer to 'induced illness' throughout their chapter.

We would support Gretchen Precey's view that:

'It is important not to look at MSBP as a behaviour in isolation, proof of which is in its own right sufficient to justify initiation of civil and possibly criminal proceedings. It is essential to consider the case in its entirety, taking note of the whole plethora of risk to which the child may be subject, not just whether or not a 'finding' of MSBP can be sustained.'

Civil liberties

The impact of whether someone is or is not diagnosed with a mental illness has a long history within the field of civil liberty. The contested nature of the diagnosis and the impact of the application of the label in relation to other people's perceptions of parenting ability, means that being accused of MSBP abuse of children has strong implications for civil liberties particularly because of its widespread association with Beverley Allitt. A campaign by the pressure group Mothers under Munchausen (MUM) highlighted the impact of alleged wrongful accusation, and Brian Morgan has written and broadcast widely on these issues.

This is compounded by the furore and hostility that has surrounded the debate about covert video surveillance as a means of protecting children which, for some, runs contrary to professional ethics (see Thomas, 1994).

Power issues and sexism

The previous section alluded to the power issues surrounding the debate over whether or not MSBP can be seen as a mental health issue.

O'Hagan (1994) has also raised concerns about powerful male paediatricians diagnosing primarily mothers. It does seem that the vast majority of perpetrators are women:

'From experience of more than 300 cases it is clear that the child's natural mother is the usual perpetrator. My experience is that it is the client's natural mother in 90% of cases, the father in 5% and another carer (for instance, a nurse or child minder in) 5%.' Meadow (1994) p. 112

The psychological profile of mothers and their relationship to their partners is described by Gray, Bentovim and Milla in Chapter 11. Less has been written about male perpetrators. Meadow notes the following characteristics:

'The male perpetrators whom I have encountered indulge in extravagant lies in relation to most aspects of their lives. They tend to deceive their wives and families about their work and lives and extend that exaggeration and fabrication to their children. They have lied about their school achievements, their sporting achievements, their past and their present life. It is common for them to be keen on first aid and to be volunteer ambulancemen or firemen. They revel in having their child suffering life threatening illnesses and in their role as resuscitators.' Meadow (1994) p. 114

Ethnicity appears to be absent from the current clinical picture. We have been unable to find a case of MSBP involving a black family.

These are some of the power issues affecting the adults' relationships. We feel that it is also important to keep in mind that the central power issue, as Martin Banks asserts in Chapter 7, is that of the oppression and abuse of defenceless children by adults who are the prime care takers for them.

Safe environments

Trust and betrayal are key themes in the investigation of MSBP abuse. The case of Beverley Allitt throws into sharp relief the wider crisis in our culture of providing safe environments for our children, as it becomes clear that all child care services have been infiltrated by those whose aim is entirely the opposite. There is a crisis of confidence caused by abusing priests, residential child care workers, teachers, nurses, and others, which we are only just beginning to face and which has the power to bring down governments, as we saw recently in Ireland. We will return to this theme in more detail in our conclusion.

We invite you to consider the possibility of some day working with a child who is the victim of MSBP abuse. We hope that this book will help you to prepare yourself for the journey you will have to undertake with this child. We also hope that it will help you to prepare yourself for some of the dilemmas you may face and make use of some of the experience that has gone before. This should enable you to ensure that you can balance appropriately the welfare and protection of the child with the carer's need for natural justice.

In seeking to do this:

'It is helpful to consider MSBP abuse as one end of the spectrum of ways in which parents behave when their child is ill. Normal anxious parents worry about their children when they are ill. Those who are particularly anxious, lonely or in difficult circumstances, may worry more and will use their doctor more. Some will perceive symptoms that others do not observe. Others, under great stress, may exaggerate some of the symptoms to try and gain more help. Many parents who do not get the help they need from one doctor will take the child to a succession of other doctors.

Similarly when a child has a genuine illness, some parents will be much more cautious than others in the way they treat that child, and will be over protective; they needlessly prolong the extent of the child's illness. These are natural ways for parents to behave and health services have a duty to be able to respond to the many different ways in which parents in different societies cope with ill children. It is only when the degree of exaggeration or deception is extreme and positively harmful to the child that it should be classified as abuse.' Meadow (1994) p. 112

We invite those of you currently facing those dilemmas to use the material we have collected together, both to assist you in your work with children and families and to act as a spur to furthering the debate.

This book is not intended to be comprehensive. We have not been able to cover all the issues we would have liked, nor have all the people we would have liked to make a contribution been able to do so. We need to acknowledge that understanding and practice in this area is still developing and we see this collection as an important contribution to that process. In the conclusion we highlight areas that merit further work and other issues that merit further exploration.

References

Bools, C N, Neale, B A and Meadow, S R (1993) 'Follow-up of victims of fabricated illness (Munchausen syndrome by proxy), *Archives of Disease in Childhood*, 69, 625-630

Department of Health (1995) *The Challenge of Partnership in Child Protection: practice guide*. HMSO

Family Rights Group (1992) *The Children Act 1989: working in partnership with families*

Feldman, M D (1995) *Patient or Pretender: inside the strange world of factitious disorders*. John Wiley

Lancet Editorial (1994) 'Spying on mothers' 4 June, 343, 8910, 1373

Meadow, S R (1994) 'Munchausen syndrome by proxy' *in* Levy, A QC (ed) *Re-focus on child abuse*. Hawksmere

O'Hagan, K (1994) 'Covert Video Surveillance "makes liars of staff"', letter in *Community Centre*, 29 September

Schreier, H A and Libow, J (1993) *Hurting for Love (Munchausen by proxy syndrome)*. Guildford Press

Thomas, T (1994) 'Covert Video Surveillance', *New Law Journal*, 15 July

Thorburn, J, Lewis, A and Shemmings, D (1995) *Paternalism or Partnership? family involvement in the child protection process*. HMSO

Thorpe, D (1994) *Evaluating Child Protection*. Open University Press

1. Munchausen syndrome by proxy: an overview

Dr Terence Stephenson, Senior Lecturer in the Department of Child Health at the University of Nottingham and Honorary Consultant Paediatrician at University Hospital Nottingham and City Hospital Nottingham

Definition of MSBP

Munchausen syndrome by proxy occurs when someone persistently fabricates symptoms on behalf of another, causing that person to be regarded as ill, or induces illness in another. The name of Baron von Munchausen, an 18th century German raconteur who told stories of fantastic travels and imaginary exploits, was first used in a medical context in 1951 by the psychiatrist Richard Asher. He used the term 'Munchausen syndrome' to describe adults who seemed to have a strange addiction to hospitals and would either fabricate illness or induce illness in themselves to enable them to be admitted to hospital and see doctors for repeated unnecessary investigations and treatment. The fact that these patients indulged in 'doctor shopping' – travelling between one hospital and another and never admitting that they had already seen several doctors previously – led Richard Asher to draw a parallel with the picaresque exploits of the characters in the tales of Baron von Munchausen (Asher, 1951). By analogy, the term 'Munchausen syndrome by proxy' (MSBP) was first adopted by Meadow in 1977, when he described the details of two families in which the children had parents who, by fabrication, had caused the children innumerable harmful medical procedures (Meadow, 1977). Using this definition, the criteria for a diagnosis of MSBP are defined as follows:

1. Illness in a child is fabricated by a parent, or someone who is acting as the child's carer.
2. The child is presented for medical assessment and care, usually persistently, often resulting in multiple medical procedures.
3. The perpetrator denies the aetiology of the illness of the child.
4. Acute symptoms and signs of illness cease when the child is separated from the perpetrator, almost always the mother (Meadow, 1982 and Rosenberg, 1987).

The prevalence of MSBP has never been ascertained. However, an estimate of the magnitude of the problem is hinted at by the work of Professor Meadow. Over a 13-year period from 1976 to 1988, he saw approximately 100 families in which the above criteria were met (Bools and others, 1992). These families were not drawn from a defined geographical population because Meadow was consulted by professional colleagues from many parts of the United Kingdom. However, it is likely that, at least in the earlier years of that period, he would have been consulted about most of the cases in the United Kingdom, as this was such a rare and novel diagnosis. Assuming that he saw only half the cases in the United Kingdom, this would suggest there were approximately 15 cases per year among a population of some seven million children under the age of ten years, the age group principally affected by MSBP.

Cases such as those involving the nurse Beverley Allitt, who was convicted of the murder of four children and the attempted murder of three other children in her care and of causing grievous bodily harm to six others, and several other cases of children's nurses harming paediatric patients in North America, are extremely rare and add little to our understanding of MSBP involving parents. There is concern that assaults by nursing staff on patients may include not only children but also the elderly. It is debatable whether cases in which nurses or others caring for children have committed murder or attempted murder should be bracketed with those of MSBP. While there is a degree of overlap, and while someone in the role of the carer does induce illness in a child, there are also a great many differences from cases in which a parent, usually the mother, persistently fabricates or induces illness in a child over a longer period.

Manifestations of MSBP

MSBP can present with a large number of different manifestations, which contributes to the difficulty in making the diagnosis.

Some examples are shown in Table 1. In some cases symptoms which the child has never complained of at all are fabricated, whereas in other cases, which are potentially more dangerous, disease or symptoms are caused deliberately by the parent administering something to the child to induce illness or harming the child by trauma or suffocation.

Table 1   Manifestations of MSBP

Fictitious symptoms	Deliberate harm
• Alleged epileptic fits. • Alleged recurrent abdominal pain. • The use of menstrual blood or blood from meat to suggest that the child is passing blood in the urine or stool. • False allegations of sexual or physical abuse. • Altering blood pressure charts, temperature charts or interfering with urine testing (eg adding blood, glucose, stones or faeces to the urine sample before it is tested by the staff).	• Starvation (or interfering with parental nutrition or withdrawing stomach contents through a naso-gastric tube). • Administration of salt solutions, laxatives, diuretics, sedative drugs, warfarin or anti-epileptic drugs. • Injection of drugs such as insulin or potassium chloride or the intravenous injection of faecal material to cause infection. • Causing bleeding from the mouth, anus, urethra, vagina, skin or from a birthmark. • Causing a rash by applying irritant substances to the skin. • Repeated suffocation.

The commonest presentations of MSBP which have been described are:

- suffocation, which may involve several hundred episodes over a period of months or years and usually involves young children;
- poisoning, which may involve older children;
- the fabrication of seizures over a period of many years, leading to extensive and inappropriate treatment and investigation for epilepsy.

Obviously, there will be a bias in the reported literature towards those cases that are most serious or dramatic or most capable of unequivocal proof. It is therefore likely that these are the tip of the iceberg and that there are many more cases of less obvious types of fabrication or induction of illness as described in Table 1. Fabrication, as opposed to induction, is much less likely to cause serious illness or fatality and many of these cases may never be detected.

Several recent cases have revolved around the distinction between the natural exaggeration a parent may use in order to expedite investigation and treatment of their child and exaggeration that is totally inappropriate and therefore constitutes MSBP. This distinction is not always easy; for example, some studies have suggested that up to ten per cent of asthmatic children are on restriction diets for which there is no medical evidence of benefit. Paediatricians and general practitioners will often have to help parents who have an inappropriately low threshold for referring their child because of relatively trivial symptoms, or to dissuade parents from pursuing interventionist treatment for conditions that are self-limiting or benign. However, at some point along the spectrum such behaviour becomes abnormal, and this has been dealt with in some detail by Eminson and Postlethwaite (1992).

Examination of the general practitioner records may give a clue as to how frequent and inappropriate the medical consultations have been. For children under two years of age, the average consultation rate initiated by the parents is four consultations per child per year with two to three consultations per child per year initiated by the doctor. From the age of two to four, three consultations per child per year are initiated by the parents and one to two per child per year initiated by the doctor (Campion and Gabriel, 1984). There is also the possibility that the child has indeed a genuine illness in addition to fabricated or induced illness. Extreme illness exaggeration by the parents of a child with a genuine chronic illness has been described as a variant of MSBP (Masterson and others, 1988). Finally, false allegations of sexual or physical abuse have also been described as a variant of MSBP (Meadow, 1993).

Many of the symptoms and illnesses described in Table 1 occur in genuine organic disease and therefore more information is required to make a diagnosis of MSBP. There are a number of features commonly found in perpetrators of MSBP (Table 2), and other clues may be gained from an analysis of the pattern of the illness (Table 3).

The characteristics of perpetrators of MSBP have recently been reviewed (Bools and others, 1994). The authors describe 47 mothers (19 of whom they interviewed personally), over half of whom

Table 2   Features commonly found in perpetrators

- Usually the child's birth mother.
- Previous paramedical training.
- May suffer from Munchausen syndrome (15-20%).
- Previous contact with a psychiatrist.
- Physical or sexual abuse as a child (25%).
- In local authority care during childhood (children's homes or foster care).
- History of conduct disorder (faecal smearing, petty crime, running away from home, teenage prostitution, arson) or previous criminal record.
- Previous overdoses or episodes of self-harm.
- Eating/weight disorders.
- The mother is more articulate, intelligent or dominant than the father and is the child's exclusive carer.

NB The absence of these features does not disprove the diagnoses.

Table 3   Clues to the diagnosis of MSBP

- An illness which is very unusual and persistent or recurrent.
- The history of clinical findings does not make sense, inconsistent histories from different observers.
- The features of the illness are only apparent when the mother is present.
- The mother is very attentive and will not leave the child but, paradoxically, is less concerned about the child's illness than the professionals caring for the child.
- The mother is happy to be in hospital and forms close relationships with the ward staff.
- The mother is unusually knowledgeable about medical problems and treatments.
- Treatment is ineffective.
- Unusual or unexplained illness or death in previous children.

were thought to have perpetrated deliberate suffocation or poisoning of their children. Forty-one of the 47 mothers had a history of a somatizing disorder (an umbrella term for illnesses with physical complaints but without an organic basis; for example, hysterical conversion, hypochondriasis and the adult Munchausen syndrome), substance abuse or self-harm. Of the 19 interviewed, only one was a teenager at the time of the fabrication (the average age of the perpetrator at the time of the abnormal behaviour was

25 years), most were married and a third had suffered physical or sexual abuse as a child themselves.

Dilemmas for medical personnel

Children's doctors and nurses spend most of their time trying to help children and parents by diagnosing and treating the illness with which they are presented. Therefore, it is not surprising that the possibility that a prolonged and difficult illness in a child may in fact have been fabricated or induced by a parent is only accepted reluctantly. There is a particular difficulty for doctors, as the corollary of making a diagnosis of MSBP is that all the tests and investigations done by the doctor have been unnecessary. In every case there is also the lingering anxiety that, if the case is referred to the child protection agencies and ultimately comes to court, other expert opinions will be sought and these may suggest an extremely rare diagnosis to explain the child's bizarre illness, which the child's own doctor has in fact missed. However, once the diagnosis of MSBP is suspected, action must be taken as the child may be at risk (Table 4).

Table 4   Factors that suggest significant danger to the child

- Abuse involving suffocation or poisoning.
- Child less than five years old.
- Previous 'cot deaths' or unexplained deaths of siblings.
- The mother has Munchausen syndrome herself.
- Denial by the mother, with lack of insight and remorse and a failure to accept responsibility for her actions.
- Fabrication by the mother persists after confrontation.
- The mother has a history of psychiatric illness, drug dependency, alcoholism or violence.

The doctor is therefore placed in the difficult situation of being both carer to the child and counsellor to the parents but also something of a detective and perhaps ultimately a witness against them. Ideally, it should be established with certainty that the suspected perpetrator is fabricating the illness or inducing the illness and a checklist is provided in Table 5.

However, as in all areas of child protection, certainty is not required to initiate child protection procedures and if on the balance of probability there is concern that the child's illness is likely to be the result of MSBP, then action must be taken. Excluding the parent is probably the greatest dilemma for medical staff and

Table 5   Confirming the diagnosis

- Obtain eye witness accounts of the illness episodes from observers rather than the suspected perpetrator.
- Ascertain whether any episodes have started in the absence of the suspected perpetrator.
- Check on personal, family and social details with relatives, the GP and social services. The perpetrator is often an inveterate liar. Obtain all existing hospital records of the child from other hospitals. Check with the police.
- Retain blood, vomit, stool and urine for analysis.
- Determine whether blood is human and whether it is from the child.
- Ensure that the suspected perpetrator cannot alter nursing charts and records.
- Undertake careful surveillance of the suspected perpetrator and child by one-to-one nursing.
- Perform covert video surveillance.
- Exclude the suspected perpetrator.

should not be undertaken by the paediatrician caring for the child alone. It is wise for the paediatrician to discuss the case with an experienced colleague and, if he or she agrees with the paediatrician's concerns, then a strategy meeting should be convened with police, social services and local authority lawyers but without informing the parents. A collective decision can then be taken about whether exclusion of the parents is the right course of action and, whilst a voluntary agreement from the parents is preferred, the action can be supported if necessary with an ex parte judicial direction. If exclusion is really thought to be necessary, a compromise – such as supervision by staff – is not appropriate, as perpetrators of MSBP abuse are often extremely devious and intelligent and the degree of supervision required cannot easily be provided on an acute paediatric ward using nursing staff.

The child protection system and MSBP

The approach to protecting children who are the victims of a parent's MSBP has been reviewed previously (Meadow, 1985; Stephenson, 1993). Following a multi-disciplinary strategy meeting to discuss the protection of the child, it will be necessary to confront the parent with the unpalatable fact that she is thought to have been lying or making her child ill. The person who undertakes this confrontation should be the paediatrician who has reached the diagnosis, usually accompanied by a social worker who has intimate knowledge of the case. It is inappropriate for the child to be sent back to the original referring centre with a diagnostic label of MSBP but with the difficult task of confrontation and subsequent management left to the referring paediatrician, who has not made the diagnosis.

In some cases, the multi-disciplinary strategy meeting may decide that other information needs to be gathered or that a period of covert video surveillance should take place (this is dealt with elsewhere in this book) and confrontation may therefore be deferred while this information is obtained. Nevertheless, during this time the child will remain at risk of further harm and there must be very close supervision indeed.

If the parents have been excluded, the child should now be safe and discussion at the case conference will centre around what should happen subsequently. The case conference has to decide about action in the following areas:

- Whether the child should remain in hospital, and for how long, or whether temporary fostering is more appropriate.
- Whether the parents can have any access. If the mother is thought to be the perpetrator, there is no particular reason why the father should be denied access but the dangers of supervised access by the mother have already been outlined above.
- Whether civil proceedings should be pursued under the Children Act.
- Whether the child is so at risk of subsequent harm that he or she should be taken into care or whether there is a realistic possibility of therapy for the perpetrator and ultimately rehabilitation.
- The assessment of other children in the extended family or other children of whom the perpetrator may have care from time to time.
- The Crown Prosecution Service, taking advice from the police, decides separately whether a criminal prosecution is indicated.

Of course not all these decisions will be taken at the initial case conference and it may only be with time that the issues become clear and the actions that are in the best interest of the child become obvious. This will be a very difficult time for all concerned, particularly the parents, but it should not be forgotten that the nursing and medical staff and social workers must support one another through what will often be a period of conflict and deep soul-searching. Perpetrators are often very credible but also manipulative and are capable of persuading professionals to take sides against one another.

Whatever arrangements are made for the subsequent care of the child, the statutory responsibilities are in the hands of social services and the local authority, not the hospital. The paediatrician must continue to oversee the child's growth, development and well-being while he or she is in foster care and on their return either to the birth parents or to adoptive parents. It is important that one paediatrician who knows the child well and is familiar with the details of the case continues to follow the child up long-term for the reasons outlined in the following section.

Research regarding prognosis

Those factors that suggest a child is at greater risk of a fatal outcome in the short- to medium-term have been listed in Table 4. These are factors which suggest a significant risk. With time, however, evidence is accumulating of the long-term morbidity to victims of MSBP who survive. Bools and others (1993) followed up 54 children on average six years after fabrication of illness had been identified. Thirty of the children were living with their biological mothers and 24 with other families. There was concern about possible further fabrication of 18 of the 30 children living with their biological mothers, and half of the children followed up had behavioural or psychological disorders that were considered to represent an unacceptable outcome.

Sadly, MSBP does not seem to be confined to a single index child within the family. The same group followed up 82 siblings of children who had been victims of fabricated illness and it was found that 11 per cent of the siblings had died in early childhood with the cause of death being uncertain. Thirty-nine per cent of siblings themselves had illnesses fabricated by their mothers and 17 per cent had been affected by either failure to thrive, non-accidental injury, inappropriate medication or neglect (Bools and others, 1992).

Conclusion

This chapter gives only a brief outline of MSBP, which is an extremely complex disorder with many medical, sociological and legal aspects that require careful consideration. There is now a limited but expanding literature available on this bizarre behaviour, those who perpetrate it and those who are the victims of it:

some of the key references are given below. Some of the continuing areas of controversy are dealt with in the subsequent chapters.

References

Asher, R (1951) 'Munchausen syndrome', *The Lancet*, 1, 339–341

Bools, C N, Neale, B A and Meadow, S R (1992) 'Co-morbidity associated with fabricated illness (Munchausen syndrome by proxy)', *Archives of Disease in Childhood*, 67, 77–79

Bools, C N, Neale, B A, Meadow, S R (1993) 'Follow-up of victims of fabricated illness (Munchausen syndrome by proxy)', *Archives of Disease in Childhood*, 69, 625–630

Bools, C N, Neale, B A, Meadow, S R (1994) 'Munchausen syndrome by proxy: a study of psychopathology', *Child Abuse and Neglect*, 18, 773–788

Campion, P D and Gabriel, J (1984) 'Child consultation patterns in general practice comparing "high" and "low" consulting families', *British Medical Journal*, 288, 1426–1428

Eminson, D M and Postlethwaite, R J (1992) 'Factitious illness: recognition and management', *Archives of Disease in Childhood*, 67, 1510–1516

Masterson, J, Dunworth, R and Williams, N (1988) 'Extreme illness exaggeration in paediatric patients: a variant of Munchausen syndrome by proxy?', *American Journal of Orthopsychiatry*, 58, 188–193

Meadow, S R (1977) 'Munchausen syndrome by proxy – the hinterland of child abuse', *The Lancet*, 2, 343–345

Meadow, S R (1982) 'Munchausen syndrome by proxy', *Archives of Disease in Childhood*, 57, 92–98

Meadow, S R (1985) 'Management of Munchausen syndrome by proxy', *Archives of Disease in Childhood*, 60, 385–393

Meadow, S R (1993) 'False allegations of abuse and Munchausen syndrome by proxy', *Archives of Disease in Childhood*, 68, 444–447

Rosenberg, D A (1987) 'Web of deceit: a literature review of Munchausen syndrome by proxy', *Child Abuse and Neglect*, 11, 547–563

Stephenson, T (1993) 'Beyond belief', *Law Society Gazette*, 90, 28–29

2. On first encountering Munchausen syndrome by proxy: a guide for beginners

Gretchen Precey, Senior Practitioner, Clermont Child Protection Unit, Brighton

'The human mind takes time to grasp a reality that is totally beyond its experience or comprehension.'

From the report of the Clothier Inquiry
into the case of Beverley Allitt

From the grandiose title of this chapter the reader may be forgiven for assuming that the writer is a person of vast experience and knowledge in the field of Munchausen syndrome by proxy (MSBP). Far from it. My knowledge is based on a single case, but a case that took a year to untangle, understand and progress. In the course of that year I became intrigued both with the dynamics of the particular case I was dealing with and also with the whole idea of mothers deliberately inducing or falsely describing illness or injury in their child.

Through working on this case, reading what little material is written on the subject, and discussing the work with colleagues, some ideas about recognition, assessment and management of MSBP have occurred to me which may also be of use to other practitioners who are placed in this situation.

This chapter will take the form of a case study in which I will describe in detail the features of the case which led the assessment team to believe that behaviour associated with MSBP was present. From the case material I will also draw on some guidelines and principles that emerged during the course of the work and some issues concerning the nature of MSBP itself and its usefulness as a discrete diagnosis.

In an attempt to maintain the anonymity of the people involved I have changed names and circumstances wherever possible without compromising information that is of clinical significance.

Outline of the case

The case first came to the attention of the Unit in Brighton two years ago. As a multi-disciplinary second tier resource serving a large county, the Unit is called in by local area social services teams to consult and assist on particularly complex cases of child abuse. In this instance we were asked to help the area team investigate the life-threatening overdose of William, aged four, that had occurred a few days earlier under extremely strange circumstances.

William had been admitted to hospital early in the morning of 13 July 1993 having been discovered convulsing and hallucinating by Karen, a family friend who was caring for William at the time. She said she found 18 Imiprimine tablets (a tricyclic anti-depressant) in the pocket of his pyjamas and on his pillow. The prescription had been made out for William's mother, Mary, who had the previous day been discharged from a psychiatric unit where she was being treated for depression.

As it was a newly prescribed bottle containing 40 tablets, Karen calculated that William must have taken up to 20 tablets. Karen took William to the casualty department of the local hospital where he required immediate resuscitation for what was described by the hospital as a near fatal overdose of a 'quantity' of Imiprimine. Following treatment, William made a complete recovery but when video interviewed a few days later by police and social services he had virtually no accurate memory of what had happened. William said he did not know how he came to take the tablets or why he was in hospital.

William's parents had been re-housed the day his mother was released from the psychiatric unit and they had asked Karen if she would look after William for an extra night so they could sort out the new flat. Karen had looked after William during the week of his mother's hospitalisation and had often cared for him for days at a time prior to that.

Karen said that Mary must have left the newly prescribed tablets at her house by mistake when she came to see William. According to Karen, Mary was notorious for being careless with her tablets and often left open bottles lying around within the children's reach. However the tablets came to be there, what was not in dispute was that Mary and her husband Tom left Karen's house after visiting William at approximately six p.m. and spent the entire night at their new flat. Nevertheless, when William took the overdose it was his mother Mary who was arrested on suspicion of attempted murder. William was placed with foster carers on an emergency protection order upon his discharge from hospital.

Despite the fact that a cursory check back through the hospital notes indicated that this was the third time in the past four months that a child in Karen's care had overdosed on tablets, all of which had been prescribed for Mary, no immediate action was taken against Karen herself at the time. Neither were any moves made to investigate the safety of her own two children, Darren, aged four, and Alan, aged 18 months. This is of even more concern because of the fact that the previous two children who overdosed whilst being cared for by Karen were her own son Darren, who had been admitted to casualty four months earlier having also ingested Imiprimine, and William, admitted to casualty just two months previously having ingested Stelazine. Although neither of these events were life-threatening in the same way as William's most recent overdose, on both previous occasions the children were very sick and required a stomach wash-out.

Although with hindsight it seems unbelievable that the case should have gone in this direction, it is not unusual in the confused, frantic response to the near death of a child in such strange circumstances that investigators travel down blind alleys in the early stages. The inability or unwillingness of professionals to see what is in front of their eyes is not an uncommon occurrence in the recognition of MSBP.

When I became involved in the case William was in foster care; his mother, Mary was on police bail under investigation for trying to murder him; Karen was at home with her two children. Also, there were unmistakable signs of a significant split in the professional group that had dealt with the case thus far. The police remained convinced of the complicity of Mary, despite the lack of any firm evidence save that the offending tablets had been prescribed to her. The doctors protested that the wrong woman was being investigated and urged that some logical thinking be done as to how four-year-olds come to overdose in the middle of the night on tablets in child-proof bottles that taste bitter. Social services knew that Mary had a history of psychiatric disturbance and there had recently been concerns for William's safety. They also knew Karen as a caring mother who had helped Mary many times in looking after William. Karen herself had considerable support from social services in parenting Darren and especially Alan, who had been born prematurely and had severe developmental delay. Not only did splits become apparent between professionals as to how the case should be taken forward, but there were also profound differences of opinion within some of the agencies. For example, the members of the police Child Protection Team were keen that Karen's possible role in the poisonings be investigated at an early stage. They were overruled by the Criminal Investigation Department who decided that the focus needed to be on Mary, hence her arrest on allegations of attempted murder.

The child protection case conference regarding William was reconvened six days after the overdose. The initial registration had been made seven weeks earlier because of Mary's deteriorating mental health which caused her to claim to hear voices that told her to strangle William. I noticed when I was going over the notes that there had in fact been a case conference several weeks prior to the one that led to registration. This very first conference was called when Karen reported to social services that she had seen William's father hit him several times in a fit of temper. That case conference did not result in registration, but what is significant is that the day after that conference William was taken to hospital with the first overdose. The recommendation of the conference which followed the second and more serious overdose was for the county to seek a care order on William and for further investigative work to be done in order to try and establish what had actually happened. An initial case conference on Darren and Alan was not held until nearly three weeks after the overdose. Among the recommendations made from that conference were that individual work be done with Karen to look at her relationship with Mary and to help her to be more assertive in determining what was right and wrong for her children and in exerting more control over her environment. It was suggested that Darren be referred for play therapy and an assessment of Karen's parenting capacity be undertaken. Again, with hindsight this appears to be a gross underestimate of what was really required.

The assessment process [phase one]

It was clear to me that what was needed was a much more thorough assessment of both families before any recommendations could be made about either returning William to his parents or considering the removal of Darren and Alan. An assessment team was formed which I coordinated.

Karen already had an allocated social worker who had known her for some time because of her long-standing difficulties in coping with Alan and Darren. It was not unknown for Karen to ring him in a panic early in the morning demanding that he come over to her flat immediately because Darren would not put on his shoes and go to school. Because of his relationship with Karen, her social worker was a key member of the assessment team and he and I jointly did the interviews with Karen in the first phase of the assessment.

Karen and her children had been supported by staff at the local family centre for several years. Their key worker at the centre was visiting Karen twice a week at home to help her bath Darren who, because of his physical problems, Karen found difficult to bath on her own. She knew all the boys well, including William, as his family were also involved in the centre's support programmes. Her role on the assessment team was to help me in my direct work with the children.

The social worker for William's family was relatively new to the case and did not have the same depth of background knowledge as the worker for Karen. She and I worked together with Mary and Tom, seeing them both individually and as a couple.

We also included the community paediatrician as part of the assessment team. She had looked after Alan since his birth and knew the history well. The consultant child psychiatrist attached to the Unit was also part of the team. He was used at first as an advisor but later became directly involved with me in interviewing Karen. Among the many benefits of having doctors on the assessment team was their ability to access and interpret previous medical records, which in this case proved crucial.

Two separate interview schedules were drawn up for each family. Karen's social worker and I interviewed Karen together weekly for six sessions. We also interviewed her estranged partner, Mike and her mother. I had two sessions with Darren, working together with the family centre worker. The social worker for William's family and I had two sessions with Mary and Tom separately and saw them together as a couple three times. I conducted two sessions with William on his own, again in conjunction with the family centre worker. His social worker and I also visited the foster carers where William was placed to obtain an independent view of his behaviour.

Written agreements were made with both families outlining the purpose of the work, which was to obtain more information about all the overdoses in order to come to some judgement of the risk posed to the children by their respective carers. The agreements also outlined the pattern and number of interviews, how the information was to be shared, and secured permission for the team to obtain information from medical records. All the work was done at the Unit and was videotaped.

We chose to interview Mike because although he was not in the household at the time – Karen having obtained an injunction against him because of his drunken, violent behaviour – he had been present on the night of the last overdose by William and was said by Karen to have been the first to find him. It was also important to ask him about the history of their relationship and his view of Karen. Karen's relationship with her mother was strained and they did not see much of each other but I remembered Professor Roy Meadow's comment that interviews with the mothers of MSBP mothers could be 'worth their weight in gold'. In this case we were struck by Karen's mother's uncanny physical similarity to her daughter both in appearance and mannerisms. She told us about her own history as a victim of sexual abuse and Karen's childhood of abuse.

The aim of speaking to Darren and William was to attempt to approach them about the previous overdoses in a more facilitative way than the formal interview process would allow. With the help of the psychiatrist, I obtained prescriptions for both Stelazine and Imiprimine to see if recognition of the tablets would help their recall of events.

Although the case took up an enormous amount of my time during the investigative stage, it seemed important that there was one coordinator who had an overview of the entire case and direct contact with all parties in order to minimise the risk of splits occurring within the professional team. Nevertheless divisions among us did occur. People who had worked with Karen and observed her investment in her children felt that she was not capable of deliberately poisoning either of them or William. They thought that Mary's mental health history was being minimised and more attention needed to be paid to her. As more information about Karen emerged, there was also a faction within the team who urged the immediate removal of her children on emergency protection orders before any more work was done. There was another lobby which favoured the conspiracy theory whereby Karen and Mary had planned the overdose together, and that perhaps there was a sexual relationship between the two women. Another potential for splits within the team was Karen's tendency to manipulate professionals. We discovered that she often played one of us off against the other, idealising some workers to the detriment of others. It became necessary for us to check with each other frequently to confirm that Karen really had been told what she said one of us had told her.

The most appropriate way of managing these divisions was

through regular meetings of the assessment team and constant communication between us about our various views. Although the debate at the meetings was often heated, it was essential that opinions were exchanged within the professional group in order to avoid our differences being played out in our work with the clients. Here again the value of having an overall coordinator for the assessment, though not always the most comfortable role to have, allowed for the progress of the work to be as focused as possible.

To support me in my position in the 'hot seat', I benefited from consultation with another child psychiatrist from outside the county who had already dealt with a number of cases involving features of MSBP. I also brought the work regularly to case discussion sessions at the Unit. I found involvement in this kind of work stressful and potentially obsessional. Skilled, regular supervision was essential for me to talk through my ideas about what was happening in the interviews and my theories about the overdoses but also for me to express my own reactions to the content of what we were dealing with both in terms of the clients and the dynamics of the assessment team.

In addition to the interviews, the other vital part of the assessment was obtaining as much background information as possible. This meant going through both medical and social work files in order to gain a more comprehensive view of past events that could give us clues to present behaviour. It was not until I began to do some careful reading of medical notes, police statements, case conference minutes and running record notes on social work case files that a clearer picture began to emerge. It was at this stage that the 'Eureka Factor' was most prominent and I shared with Professor Meadow what he described as a sense of excited curiosity akin to following the trail in a murder mystery, which overtook him when he first began to piece together evidence and look at a child's medical history in a different light.

As Karen had been known to social services and had lived locally for many years, there was much more information about her. Mary had come to the county from Ireland five years before and had not had the same amount of contact with statutory agencies, so there was not as much known about her from outside sources.

From my research and interviews with Karen the following chronology of events emerged (Table 6).

It is probably obvious to the seasoned child protection worker what risks were illustrated in Karen's history: undisclosed incest over a period of years; pregnancy by her own father, affecting her own self-image as victim; the sodium overdose and further harm-

Table 6   Karen: chronology of events

	06/12/64	Karen born – RAF family – 16 moves, 8 schools – age 9 began a series of admissions to child psychiatric units because of withdrawn behaviour
1980		Overdosed
1984		Overdosed [3 months in psychiatric hospital]
1985		Pregnant with own father's baby, precipitated disclosure of years of sexual abuse by him and his friends.
	August	Overdosed [wanted to kill herself and baby out of guilt about the conception].
	05/10/85	William (1) born at 37 weeks. Karen and baby placed with foster carers.
	31/12/85	William (1) [13 weeks] admitted to hospital. Dehydrated, vomiting, convulsing. Found to have excessive sodium levels. Discharged 07/01/86.
1986	08/01/86	William (1) re-admitted to hospital with high sodium levels. Removed from Karen's care on a place of safety order.
	30/05/86	Karen joins William (1) at new foster placement.
	15/06/86	William (1) admitted to hospital with severe sunburn.
	20/06/86	Karen attempts to put William (1) in a bath full to the top with cold water. Discovered by foster carer.
	03/07/86	Karen attempts to suffocate William (1) with a pair of knickers. Discovered by foster carer.
	04/07/86	Karen admitted to psychiatric unit. William (1) on full care order, later adopted.
1988	04/11/88	Elizabeth born [term]. Died at 5 days of neo-natal meningitis.
1989	25/09/89	Darren born [28 weeks]. Discharged after two months in hospital.
	02/12/89	Darren on emergency admission to hospital for inguinal hernia operation.
1990	January	Miscarriage.
	23/02/90	Darren admitted to casualty – vomiting.
	04/06/90	Darren admitted to casualty – suspected non-accidental injury to head.
	28/11/90	Darren admitted to casualty – ingestion of mouse poison.
	December	Emma born – stillbirth.

Table 6   Karen: chronology of events (*continued*)

1991	Autumn	William (2) born [27 weeks]. Died one day later.
1992	30/05/92	Alan born [26 weeks]. Global development delay, Karen and Alan in hospital in London for five months following the birth.
1993	28/03/93	Overdose by Darren [Imiprimine].
	03/04/93	Alan admitted to hospital, Karen could not cope.
	04/04/93	Alan discharged. Karen admitted to hospital with symptoms of drug overdose but blood test clear.
	05/04/93	William (son of Mary) admitted to hospital having been in Karen's care the previous day, struggling, trembling, stiffness. Toxicology screen clear.
	10/05/93	Overdose by William (son of Mary) [Stelazine].
	13/07/93	Overdose by William (Imiprimine).
	15/07/93	Mary arrested on suspicion of attempted murder of William. William on emergency placement order.
	12/08/93	Assessment commences.
	25/09/93	William returned home.
	02/10/93	Darren and Alan removed on emergency placement orders and placed with foster carers.

ful, surreptitious behaviour toward her first child; the number of injuries to Darren in his early years; frequent pregnancies necessitating separation from Darren and the birth of a child with severe disabilities in a family whose resources for coping were already very stretched.

Translating those events into a genogram, Karen's history is shown in Figure 2. The genogram for Mary and Tom (Figure 1) is in no way as complicated.

No similar pathology was evident in Mary's past. Her childhood was marred by her parent's acrimonious relationship and divorce when she was young. Her mother died when Mary was a teenager and she soon left home to work in a series of residential facilities for children with disabilities in Ireland. She was dismissed from one of her jobs following the near drowning of an 11-year-old boy with cerebral palsy when she was bathing him. Mary said the incident occurred when she was very tired having just come off a

Figure I   Genogram for Mary and Tom

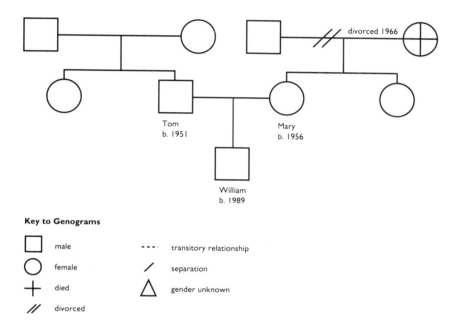

Tom
b. 1951

Mary
b. 1956

William
b. 1989

Key to Genograms

□	male	- - - -	transitory relationship
○	female	/	separation
+	died	△	gender unknown
//	divorced		

series of night duties and her own mental health was not good. She says she temporarily blacked out and when she came to, the boy was under the water. She was suspended and an investigation ensued. There were no criminal charges brought but she was asked to leave the institution. Independent checks confirm the content of her story.

It was shortly after this that Mary came to southern England, this time choosing deliberately to do residential work with the elderly rather than children. She met Tom via an advertisement in the personal columns. She was pregnant with William within a month of their introduction. Mary was highly ambivalent about the prospect of motherhood but, although her father urged her to have a termination, she and Tom decided to have the baby. After William's birth Mary suffered a severe post-natal depression requiring her to remain in hospital for several months.

Unlike Mary's account of the events of her life, especially the accident with the boy in her care, interviews with Karen were much less straightforward. Karen has virtually no memory of the

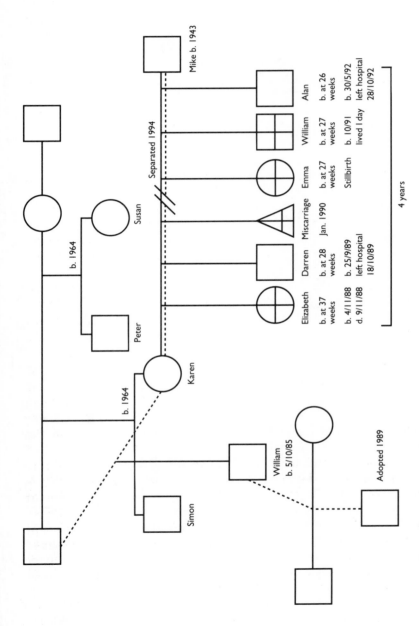

Figure 2 Genogram for Karen

events surrounding the sodium overdose of her first child William (1). She has never taken responsibility for putting salt in his milk, although reading reports written at the time the implication is that she tampered with his feeds. Karen at first denied and then could not remember what happened to her child William (1). It was the discovery of this event and its circumstances that generated considerable anxiety within the team for the safety of her two children living at home.

Six weeks into the assessment process it had become clear that the person who was the greater risk to children was Karen and not Mary. Our recommendation was that William be returned to his parents immediately while still remaining on a supervision order and that his name be kept on the child protection register until the work was complete.

Our concerns about Karen mounted daily until it was evident to us that we had no choice but to remove her two children. Our preferred method of achieving this was through planned emergency protection orders. The reason why we felt that emergency protection orders rather than accommodation was necessary was because of our uncertainty as to how Karen would react to more confrontational questioning. Throughout the work thus far Karen was overtly passive but this masked an underlying hostile compliance with the assessment process. Her tendency to manipulate information and deliberately misinform us about what another member of the assessment team had said to her was, I believe, a measure of her true feelings about the process. As a victim of prolonged sexual abuse, Karen was accustomed to 'doing as I am told'. Up to this point our work with her had been mainly information gathering. She cooperated with our questions although the answers were often 'don't know/can't remember' delivered in a flat monotone with no eye contact.

Once the pattern of her past behaviour became clearer, we knew that the assessment work needed to become more direct and that we had to tell Karen that we suspected that she had deliberately poisoned her first child William (1), and had also more recently poisoned both Darren and Mary's son William, nearly killing him. Because we did not know how destabilising this process would be for Karen and what the effect of that would be on her own children, our decision was to remove the children before the new phase of the work began. In planning the sequence of events in this way, I was cognisant of the advice of other professionals, such as Dr Arnon Bentovim, Dr Herbert Schreier and Judith Libow, who recommend that plans for the custody and safety of the child and siblings must be in hand before the mother is confronted.

The assessment process [phase two]

From this point the work changed significantly in terms of our approach to Karen. Instead of working jointly with her social worker, I now interviewed her with the consultant child psychiatrist attached to the Unit. It seemed important to separate the direct work with her that needed to be more challenging and confrontative, from the day-to-day arrangements for the children and their contact with her now that they were in care. We felt it was too confusing for her social worker to play both roles. The psychiatrist had previous experience of working with another mother with MSBP behaviour and his introduction to the sessions helped to mark the changed nature of the work with Karen.

Thus began what for me was the most difficult aspect of the work. We met with Karen for five fortnightly sessions over ten weeks. During this time Karen also had weekly sessions with a forensic clinical psychologist who had originally been commissioned to give us an assessment of Karen's intellectual capacity and cognitive ability. Karen said she found his sessions helpful and that she felt that he understood her. We debated about the wisdom of Karen seeing two separate sets of therapists but concluded that the psychologist provided a supportive antidote to our more pressurised, direct way of working with her.

This is consistent with the Hollerden/Hersch technique designed to help patients with factitious disorders, as described by Schreier and Libow (1993), whereby two therapists see one client and split their roles into 'helper' and 'confronter'. The goal is to develop a supportive alliance with the patient, while still addressing the reality of the problem. This dynamic was also manifested in our joint work: I tended to take the role of confronter and the psychiatrist was the helper. There is little in the literature about effective therapeutic techniques with MSBP mothers, largely because there have not been many documented clinical accounts. Much of what is around relates to work with Munchausen patients and even then there is disagreement about therapeutic techniques:

> 'If anything positive is to happen it will only come through timely, vigorous and repeated confrontation about the true nature of the patient's illness.' (Stone 1977)

whereas Fras (1978) recommends,

'... a very supportive, cautious psychotherapy aimed at maintaining the relationship with the patient and not challenging too vigorously or for too long a period.'

The literature that is available regarding therapy with MSBP patients is largely based on descriptions of individual cases. These reveal emerging parallels in therapy between sexual abuse work and MSBP.

'Her attitude reminded me of men involved in sexual offences. They use denial and always represent themselves as the victim. Sometimes they have been victimised as children, but it is still a diversion away from their own responsibility.' (Schreier and Libow, 1993, p. 154)

'I felt she was either lying to me or in such a dissociated state that maybe she needed extra help.' (Schreier and Libow, 1993, p. 156)

A number of clinicians reported MSBP mothers who, when confronted with the evidence, denied conscious agency; for example, 'I must have done it but I can't remember a thing'.

One pattern that does emerge is the unlikelihood of full admission when the mother is confronted, even when that confrontation is backed up by strong evidence. This has certainly been our experience with Karen. She insisted that William in his first overdose ate the Stelazine tablets 'like Smarties' right in front of her. Karen was convinced that Mary and her carelessness with tablets caused William's second overdose, although she knew Mary was not in the house when it happened. She denied, passively but persistently, that she could have committed the acts we believe she perpetrated. Her view was that we thought she poisoned the children because of the things that had happened in her past, particularly the abuse by her father and the sodium overdose of her first child.

The potential for the development in the worker of an intensely negative response to the MSBP mothers with whom they deal is mentioned by several therapists, who report feelings of anger and hostility toward their client in these cases. At the other end of the spectrum are the counter-transference issues associated with the strong desire to believe that these conscientious, insistent parents are indeed being wrongly accused. The maintenance of therapeutic objectivity is a difficult balance to achieve. I found myself becoming very angry with Karen in sessions, partly out of frustration at her passivity and refusal or inability to remember and her superficial but hostile compliance.

After several sessions of feeling we were getting nowhere, even in the face of what seemed to me to be incontrovertible evidence that pointed to Karen's complicity in the poisonings, we decided to increase the level of confrontation by playing to her some of the extracts from the tape of one of my sessions with William. As mentioned previously, part of the assessment process was to talk again with Darren and William separately about how they had each come to take the tablets. These sessions were largely inconclusive, with each boy saying Mary had given them the tablets, then that Karen had, and also simply saying that they just did not know what happened. One particular conversation with William did yield more spontaneous information, when he described Karen crushing tablets with her hand. This was especially significant, since part of Karen's defence was that due to an injury to her right arm sustained seven years before, the arm was largely useless, making it impossible for her to open child-proof bottles or crush tablets. The state of Karen's arm varied drastically during the time we saw her. At times it was strapped tightly to her chest, the fingers almost blue; at other times she appeared to have good use of it, although she always denied this. Her incapacity seemed directly related to how helpless she was feeling. A report from the neurologist who treated her at the time indicated that although some nerve damage was sustained, there was no medical reason why she should not make a full recovery.

It was with all these things in mind that I played Karen the tape of my conversation with William, hoping that this, if nothing else, would elicit an admission. Despite seeing the tape in which William describes Karen taking the top off the tablet bottle and using it to crush the tablets, she still insisted that would be an impossibility for her because of her damaged arm. William also said that Karen would get into trouble if he told. She said she did not know what he was talking about there. Both the psychiatrist and I suggested to her that in our experience of how young children come to take overdoses there were many things about her account that simply did not make sense. For example, that a child would not deliberately take a number of tablets that did not taste good and that he would wake up out of a sound sleep, search through a drawer in order to find the bottle, and open a child-proof top in order to do it. Not deterred by what seemed to us to be logic, Karen steadfastly insisted that the overdose had happened exactly as she had described it, with Mike finding William fitting and hallucinating at four a.m., the empty tablet bottle on his bed and a number of tablets strewn around his pillow and in the pocket of his pyjamas.

As this line of questioning with Karen continued, it became evident to us that the necessity of 'proving' the presence of MSBP was becoming less and less relevant.

The most acute risk to the safety of the children was a recurrence of Karen's proclivity to poison children in her care when she felt under stress. Also emerging, however, was a picture of a defeated, overwhelmed woman who was finding it increasingly impossible to deal with the demands of her children. Karen envisioned her situation as continuing to deteriorate and her need for help from social services continuing to increase as the boys grew older. This illustrates another feature of work with MSBP mothers: the importance of not neglecting other pathology in the relationship between parents and children that is also a source of significant harm. Eventually we came to the conclusion that, while features of MSBP in Karen's behaviour were of immediate concern, the basis of our recommendation for permanent separation from her children was the desperately poor prognosis for her to parent her children successfully because she herself was so needy.

In another significant interview with Karen, we discussed the reason why she had experienced so many pregnancies, many of them resulting in babies who did not survive. She told us that in fact she had never had any wish to have children. The pregnancies were all forced upon her as a result of unwanted sex with Mike, mainly when he was drunk and violent. She said that she had tried various forms of contraception but 'nothing worked'. Karen said she felt angry about the pregnancies and that being a parent was a situation that had been forced upon her by Mike's behaviour, not her own desires. She was able to admit eventually that she had mixed feelings about the children being in care and that one of those feelings was relief.

Part of our assessment also had to be an evaluation of how Darren and Alan coped without their mother. Darren, although saying he missed his mother, became very frustrated and angry when on contact visits she took more notice of the foster carer than him and did not seem to know how to relate to him. Alan's physical health and development level improved significantly within weeks of being in care. He put on weight and became more confident and more responsive to outside stimulation. The paediatrician described him as a 'different child'. Although his developmental delay and motor problems are still significant, his potential now appears to be being realised. His anxious attachment to Karen was painfully illustrated at a case conference held just two weeks after coming into care. Karen and the foster mother sat side by side at the meeting, with Alan playing on the floor. He consistently went to the foster mother for comfort and help, ignoring Karen completely, much to her distress.

Taking all of these factors into consideration, the assessment team believed that we had no alternative but to recommend full care orders on both children with a view to their adoption. A number of factors influenced our decision in coming to this conclusion:

- The children involved were all very young with little ability to understand or communicate effectively about what was being done to them.
- The abuse was severe and life-threatening.
- There had been previous harm to another child in the past that was nearly terminal.
- Karen showed no understanding about her behaviour and continued to fabricate even when confronted with the evidence.
- Karen had a number of other mental health problems, many of them the legacy of her own sexual abuse including the somatism of her difficulties into physical symptoms; for example, her paralysed arm.
- Alan had genuine medical difficulties which would require continuing care and hospital contact. It would be difficult to distinguish how much his future progress might be compromised by his mother's dependency on the hospital for support.
- Karen showed few strategies in coping with stress other than to become increasingly reliant on outside agencies to help her.

The main factor for us, however, was Karen's lack of basic parenting skills and our pessimism that she could ever acquire them because of her lack of feeling for the children and her own overwhelming emotional needs.

As with so many decisions in social work when the parents themselves are the product of dysfunctional families, it was difficult as professionals not to feel that we were yet another in the long line of abusers encountered by Karen, who had succeeded in removing everything that was hers. It was with no sense of victory that, after a five-day hearing, the judge found in favour of the county council and made full care orders on both children. The criminal evidence was not strong enough for prosecution, which is often the case with MSBP. Once the assessment began, the role of the police in the proceedings was minimal. The police personnel who worked regularly with the child protection team were supportive of our recommendations and agreed that if, in the interests of justice, Karen needed to be punished then the permanent removal of her children was enough. The Criminal Investigation

Department, who also had contact with the case, still felt that Mary must have had something to do with the overdose because her tablets were used but they conceded that there was not sufficient evidence to pursue this belief.

A question I have been asked subsequently is my view of what should happen if Karen has another child. Although I am aware of the strong desire in many parents to replace children 'lost' to care, I am not sure that Karen will set out deliberately to have more children. This also depends on the nature of her future relationships and on the degree of conscious choice she has in the matter. If she does conceive again we would of course have to assess her circumstances at the time, try to understand the meaning this child may have for her and judge how much progress she has made in understanding her past behaviour. My immediate response would be to convene a pre-birth case conference, to do a thorough assessment of her situation and consider placement at birth if nothing of significance had changed.

Learning points

One of the main issues that most exercised the minds of the assessment team was the question of motivation. What was it that caused Karen to behave in this way to children in her care? Did she have any conscious agency at all over her actions or was she so dissociated, as a result of a childhood of sexual abuse, that she genuinely had no memory of poisoning the children? Can we make a case for Karen's need to be in contact with doctors and hospitals as the crucial factor in her motivation? Was this a dysfunctional cry for help when she believed no one was listening to her?

In the literature on Munchausen syndrome, the main pay-off for the victim is described as the medical attention gained by fantasising or deliberately inducing symptoms so as to be an object of interest to the hospital, often several hospitals, and to receive treatment. For Schreier and Libow this is also the defining feature in MSBP.

> 'The critical dynamic is the mother's intense need to be in a relationship with doctors and/or hospitals...the child as a *person* means less to these parents than the child as an *object* to be used to manipulate an intensely ambivalent relationship with the physician...'

The reason for the obsession with physicians is that the mother wishes to connect to a powerful and unattainable person – the doctor – who, in fantasy, can repair earlier experienced trauma. Schreier and Libow feel the tendency for MSBP mothers is to seek the support not of family, who typically have neglected or abused her in the past, or her partner, who tends to be distant and unavailable, but of the newly-found idealised parent: the doctor.

What is the evidence for this being the defining criteria in Karen's case? Certainly, as a teenager her admission to child and adolescent units rescued her temporarily from the abuse by her father. Her first child, William, was born when Karen was living in a mother and baby foster placement where she said she was ignored and not given the help she needed. Perhaps her recourse to rescue once again was to make William ill enough so they could both be admitted to hospital and this is why she put salt in his milk. When they returned to the placement after seven days in hospital and still no notice was taken of them, she tampered with his feed the next day in order to be re-admitted to a place where they both could be cared for properly.

It also seems significant that Karen idealised her relationships with many of the doctors and nurses who treated her. Although her memory for detail in most of the events in her life was very poor, she was able to recall verbatim conversations with the registrar who looked after her during Alan's birth. Karen felt she was being treated as a special case by this female doctor, who promised her that her baby would be safe. Karen said that the doctor even visited her specially in London when she had to be transferred there for the delivery. Her frequent hospital stays with Alan because of his organic difficulties have been significant to Karen because they have brought her into relationships with nurses who care for both Alan and her. This extends to some of the nurses being described by Karen as personal friends who have come to stay with her at home at weekends.

Although not having a medical background herself (mothers with medical training, especially nursing, is often a feature of MSBP), Karen spent a significant amount of time in hospitals. It could be argued that hospitals were a refuge for Karen from the abusing men in her life, first her father and then her partner Mike, and they provided the total care she needed in times of great stress: for example, in caring for her first child, William. If that is the case, then Karen herself has no insight into her motivation. Her view of the reason for her many pregnancies was her abuse by Mike. Any suggestion made to her during our work that hospital could have been a sanctuary for her was rejected.

What are we to make of Karen's obstetric history in which she experienced six pregnancies in four years from which there were four live births but only two surviving children, one of whom was severely disabled? Most of the pregnancies were complicated and required prolonged hospital stays. There is nothing on the hospital records to indicate that Karen took any action herself deliberately to influence the course of her pregnancies or cause premature onset of labour, but then neither was the hospital at the time looking for anything other than physiological explanations for her obstetric difficulties.

One of the most dangerous features of MSBP is the length of time it takes to recognise the condition for what it is. Rosenberg (1987) estimates mean time of diagnosis to be 14.9 months. Other estimates speak of 33 per cent of cases taking more than six months to be recognised and 19 per cent over a year to be identified.

It is also a matter of speculation as to whether Darren's other appearances at casualty as a baby (see chronology) were also motivated by Karen's need for hospital contact. Darren was operated on for an inguinal hernia at the age of 18 months because of Karen's complaint that he was chronically constipated. Yet a note on the records from the family centre made at the time states that staff changing Darren's nappy, which contained a full bowel movement, were puzzled at Karen's description of Darren as constipated.

On rare occasions Karen showed the anger which could have acted as a trigger to her behaviour towards Darren. She acknowledged being angry that social services had promised her help with William when she was placed with him in the care of foster parents. Her experience was that no one was listening to her when she said the foster carers were always out and left her to get on with his care on her own. Karen also describes being angry with Mary and Tom, who she felt were dumping William on her against her wishes. On the night of William's overdose he had already been staying with Karen for a week. Both he and her own children had been ill with flu during that time and everyone in the household was exhausted. She felt unable to tell them to stop taking advantage of her. Because of Karen's history as a victim, her ability to be assertive and resist exploitation by others was limited. Perhaps the poisoning of the children was the only vehicle through which she could express her anger both towards Mary and Tom and towards social services, who she believed were not giving her the help that she needed. 'What do I have to do to get you to take notice of me?' may have been her cry as she administered the tablets. But, if this was the case, she herself is not able to make the connection.

The other hypothesis discussed by the team to help us to understand Karen's motivation was the significance of the name William. It could be that she had a whole host of different associations with that name, in view of the fact that William was the name she gave the child she had with her own father and who was later lost to her through adoption. Karen's poisoning of his feeds with salt may have had more to do with William being a living reminder of the years of abuse by her father than a cry for help or a need to be cared for by the medical profession. The fact that she also named her fifth child William (a baby born at 27 weeks who lived for one day) may also indicate unresolved feelings in Karen about the loss of the first William. How significant is it that Mary's child, who was nearly killed, was also named William? It could be mere coincidence or it could be relevant to her motivation. Whichever is the case, Karen herself can make no links.

Relevance of the label MSBP

The main plank of the defence argument in Karen's case was to prove that she was not suffering from MSBP. Their logic was that if the diagnosis was not proven, then Karen must be seen as a safe parent who was capable of looking after her children. Karen was sent to London for a two-hour interview with an adult psychiatrist who specialised in patients with Munchausen syndrome. His conclusion was that Karen did not show signs of MSBP for the following reasons:

- There was no hostility or breakdown in communication in the relationship between Karen and the doctors who were caring for Alan. According to this specialist, the typical pattern with MSBP is for the mother to be constantly at odds with the doctors and dissatisfied with the care her child receives.
- Karen did not present persistently for medical assessment. She did not attempt to hide the fact that the children had been poisoned. (But she *did* attempt to hide the identity of the poisoner which in all probability was herself.)
- The victim was not her own child, which is atypical of MSBP. (Yet some of the victims *were* her own children, her son William and Darren had both been poisoned.) Professor Meadow's study has found that 95 per cent of MSBP perpetrators are women; 90 per cent of these are the child's own mother.
- Karen could talk freely about her emotional problems. In the experience of the specialist, this is unusual in MSBP behaviour.

What is dangerous in trying to prove the presence of MSBP in a particular patient is the lack of an agreed criteria for the precise symptoms that are diagnostic of the condition. MSBP is logically a condition found in the child victim rather than the adult perpetrator. Just as we would not say that an adult perpetrator 'suffers from child sexual abuse', it is not logical to describe an adult as 'having' MSBP: it is the child upon whom the adult acts who acquires the condition. Professor Meadow has speculated that one reason why MSBP has received an adult psychiatric label is to give it the status of a listing in the DSM-III, the bible of American psychiatric syndromes, which makes it official and therefore makes treatment claimable under United States health insurance legislation.

I agree that it is important not to look at MSBP as a behaviour in isolation, proof of which is in its own right sufficient to justify initiation of civil and possibly criminal proceedings. It is essential to consider the case in its entirety, taking note of the whole plethora of risk to which the child may be subject, not just whether or not a 'finding' of MSBP can be substantiated. That was certainly a feature of our work with Karen and her children. As the case progressed, the need to prove that Karen was a perpetrator of MSBP became less and less relevant compared to the other pathology in Karen's parenting that was uncovered in the course of the assessment work. While I believe that it is helpful to think of MSBP as a spectrum of behaviours that can lead to the deliberate harm of children rather than as a dichotomous condition that is either present or absent in a perpetrator, I do think that a case can be made for the specific study of MSBP as a pattern worthy of consideration in its own right. By whatever name it is called, practitioners in child protection need to be aware of the possibility that 'good' parents are also capable of harming their children by such methods as the deliberate introduction of toxins, suffocation, fantasisation of symptoms or tampering with a child's medical treatment so as to impede recovery. The particular features of duplicity, sabotage and intrigue that usually accompany this form of child abuse, not to mention the often fatal outcome for the child if recognition comes too late, make MSBP a unique reality that is worthy of special study.

In the six years during which the Unit has been open, we have dealt with only three cases that we recognised as having features of MSBP. It would seem that this is indeed a rare and unusual form of child abuse, but one that requires an exceptional degree of investigation, planning and communication among the professional group if a safe and successful outcome is to be achieved.

This has been my account of my first experience of working with MSBP. I recognise that the writing of it has been in itself cathartic for me in processing my thoughts and responses to working with the case. I hope it has also gone some way to illuminate this most complex area of child protection work for practitioners who encounter their own cases in the future.

Acknowledgement

Arnon Bentovim, Consultant Child Psychiatrist, for the benefit of experience and generous support.

References

Fros, J (1978) 'Factitial Disease: An Update', *Psychosomatics*, 19(2), 119–122

Meadow, S R (1994) *Current Knowledge – Current Practice in Informing the Way Ahead.* Speech at MSBP conference, October 1994

Rosenberg, P (1987) 'Web of Deceit: A Literature Review of MSBP', *Child Abuse and Neglect*, 11, 547–563

Schreier, H and Libow, J (1993) *Hurting for Love (Munchausen syndrome by proxy).* Guildford Press

Stone, F (1989) 'Munchausen by proxy syndrome: An unusual form of child abuse.' Social Casework, *The Journal of Contemporary Social Work*

3. Practical concerns about the diagnosis of Munchausen syndrome by proxy

Dr Colin Morley, Honorary Consultant Paediatrician, Addenbrookes Hospital, Cambridge

[This paper was published in part in the Archives of Disease in Childhood 1995, 72, 6, 528–530.]

The purpose of this chapter is to share my concerns about the difficulties and pitfalls involved in making the diagnosis of Munchausen syndrome by proxy (MSBP) in general and in particular with regard to suffocation.

Concern about the use of the label Munchausen syndrome by proxy

Following the erroneous suggestion that Beverley Allitt had MSBP – the Clothier Report refers to her as a 'serial killer' – (Allitt Inquiry, 1994) this diagnosis has become charged with emotion and those who are now accused are tarnished with her reputation. The label Munchausen syndrome by proxy gives no indication about what happened to the child. As a substitute, I suggest that the exact nature of the problem should be stated: for example, suffocation, poisoning, putting blood in the urine, or falsely reporting fits. The label Munchausen syndrome by proxy is emotive and catchy but should now be dropped.

Concern about the criteria for diagnosing MSBP

It has been suggested that the term can be used if the following criteria are fulfilled (Meadow, 1994). However, these are non-specific and can be both misinterpreted and over-interpreted.

'*The illness is fabricated by the parent or carer.*' A mother may superficially appear to the doctors to fabricate her child's symptoms when in reality they have not listened carefully to her story. Many mothers, particularly those whose children have been ill, are simply over-anxious and are trying to get the doctor to listen to them. Some, like many of us, use exaggeration as part of their normal language.

'*The child is presented to doctors, usually persistently.*' The frequency of mothers presenting their children for medical care is not known and therefore we do not know what is normal or abnormal. Some mothers maintain their children are never ill and anxious mothers request advice almost weekly. This is the common experience of many general practitioners. Children who are seen frequently may of course genuinely be ill.

'*The perpetrator (initially) denies causing the child's illness.*' The 'perpetrator' may genuinely be innocent and that is why she persistently and vehemently denies harming her child. I am concerned that in some cases the mothers are told they have to confess to harming their child before they can have treatment and if they do not confess they are unlikely to have their children back. This is a form of blackmail and may result in a false confession from a mother desperate to get her child back at any cost. Surely the support, counselling and therapy needed by many of these mothers can be started and may continue without a 'confession'.

'*The illness clears up when the child is separated from the perpetrator.*' The illness clearing up when the child is separated from the 'perpetrator' needs to be considered carefully. Many childhood illnesses get better with time. Some conditions, such as apnoea or vomiting, improve towards the end of the first year, just about the time many of these children are taken into care. If the underlying problem is really the mother's anxiety about her child, the symptoms she is worried about may not be considered abnormal by a different carer and therefore will 'disappear' when the child is removed.

Concern about assessment indicators with regard to fabricated symptoms

The following 'diagnostic pointers' have been recommended (Samuels and Southall, 1992). At first glance these seem useful. However, when they are examined carefully they are non-specific and may be misleading to the unwary.

- '*Inconsistent histories from different observers.*' The interpretation of whether histories are inconsistent depends on how they were obtained and whether the same questions were asked in the same way.

- *'Symptoms and signs that are unusual or bizarre and inconsistent with known pathophysiology.'* The interpretation of these depends on the experience of the doctor. As experienced paediatricians know, the patients rarely seem to read the same textbooks as ourselves.

- *'Observations and investigations inconsistent with parental reports or the condition of the child.'* This may simply be because of the way the parent was asked to report the event. Mothers are not aware that they should give a scientifically accurate report to the admitting doctors. Some mothers are poor at giving a detailed account of a life-threatening event and may not appreciate that the details of time, sequence and place are vitally important. Often the busy and inexperienced junior doctors do not pursue the details as carefully as they should.

- *'Treatments which are ineffective or poorly tolerated.'* This is common and cannot be a useful diagnostic sign.

- *'Symptoms or signs which **begin** only in the presence of one parent/carer.'* Most concerned mothers are with their ill child all the time. It would be surprising if they were not the first witness of an event.

- *'Parents who are unusually calm for the severity of illness.'* Parents who appear outwardly calm may be suffering inner turmoil.

- *'Parents who are unusually knowledgeable about the illness and its repercussions.'* This is common in concerned parents and those with a chronically ill child, particularly if they have been properly informed by the doctors.

- *'Parents who fit in contentedly with ward life and [are pleased with] attention from staff.'* This is common when the children have been in a ward several times or where the ward is well organised and the staff caring and compassionate.

- *'Unusual or unexplained illness or death in previous children.'* It is important not to jump to conclusions but to investigate the details of the deaths or illnesses.

- *'Parents who have a history of unusual illness or themselves were abused as children.'* This needs careful history-taking, scrutiny of the notes or confidential discussion with the mother's doctors.

- *'Parents who have a history of conduct or eating disorders.'* These are relatively common in the community. Most of these people do not abuse their children.

The accuracy and predictive value of these diagnostic pointers are not known. As MSBP is very rare, these pointers are much more likely to be associated with normal behaviour and common illnesses. Careless use of such indicators without realising their non-specific nature may lead to mothers being falsely accused and their children taken into care.

Concern about 'exaggeration' being labelled MSBP

MSBP is being used to describe the behaviour of mothers who exaggerate a child's symptoms. This is a cause for concern because mothers frequently exaggerate their child's symptoms, not through any malignant desire to mislead the doctor but as part of common language: 'he hasn't eaten a thing all week', 'he vomits up all the feed'. Such phrases are part of everyday life and experienced paediatricians do not take the mother's story at face value but take a careful history to find out exactly what has been happening. We have no idea how common it is for mothers to exaggerate their children's symptoms. If exaggeration is included in MSBP, this will devalue the diagnosis and more mothers will be accused.

Concern about inadequate history taking

MSBP is a very serious diagnosis because the outcome for the child and family may mean care orders, separation and even criminal prosecution. It is primarily a medical diagnosis and must be based on sound medical practice. This means taking an extremely careful history and eliciting exact details about what has happened (Working Party of the BPA, 1994). It may mean talking to the mother for a long time in order to gain a clear understanding about all the episodes, why she is concerned and her own background. Unfortunately, in some cases I have known the senior doctors have hardly talked to the mother. In a recent case, the mother briefly saw the consultant during the children's illnesses but he did not take time to sit down and talk with her until he came with a social worker to say she was accused of MSBP. This is indefensible. My experience is that some mothers repeatedly take their child to the family doctor or paediatrician because they are anxious. Some are naturally anxious, some have hypochondria and others are anxious because their children have previously been very ill. The doctor realises the illnesses are trivial and repeatedly tells the mother not to worry. If the doctor had taken the time, in the early part of the illness, to take a full history, to explain what was happening, to understand why she was so concerned, and support the mother, he might have been able to prevent many of the repeated presentations and the subsequent accusation of MSBP.

Concern about the technique of covert video surveillance (CVS)

This technique involves admitting a child and mother to a cubicle equipped with covert video cameras. In many investigations where suffocation or similar abuse is expected, the child is kept in view of the cameras by being kept on or near the bed attached to a physiological recording apparatus which records heart rate, body movement, breathing patterns and oxygen levels. The lighting in the room allows recording 24 hours a day. The mother sleeps on a bed in the cubicle with the child. The video recordings are viewed continuously by two observers in another cubicle, who keep notes of everything that happens, unknown to the mother. If they think the child is being harmed, they push an alarm bell and a senior nurse intervenes.

I have several practical concerns about this technique.

- Before CVS is used in the investigation of suspected acute life-threatening events, *overt* video should be used. This might show a genuine and natural cause which the doctors can discuss with the mother. Many mothers will willingly cooperate with this and if necessary it could be done at home. Covert video surveillance is often undertaken because the history or physiological recordings have been suspicious but not conclusive. Under these circumstances, there is no reason why video surveillance needs to be covert.

- The investigators cannot allow the child to be harmed. If they see what appears to be the onset of suffocation, they can only wait a few seconds before summoning help. This means that only the start is witnessed. The assumption has to be made that if the mother continued with what she was doing, the child would have been suffocated. This is, of course, open to interpretation and speculation. One can imagine situations where covert observations by personnel trained to be suspicious of what a mother might be doing to her baby might make them think the mother was starting to suffocate the child: she might be cuddling a fussing child into her breast; playing with the child by putting her hand over his face; or bending over him to clean his face with a cloth while he struggles. Denial that this was a suffocation attempt could be considered 'typical' of MSBP and it could be difficult for the mother to defend herself.

- If CVS is only carried out when there is a high degree of suspicion that the parent is attempting to suffocate the child, then it is being used specifically to catch or entrap the parent abusing the child. This puts the child in danger. In some cases it has resulted in the child being harmed.
- The mother and child can only be admitted to the video cubicle by suggesting to the mother that further investigations need to be undertaken. If the staff really believe the child is well and the mother is harming the child, this is a deception.
- As the purpose of CVS is to watch the mother's actions, she has to be kept with the child most of the time. She is not directly told to stay with the child but feels constrained to do so in case the alarm goes off on the physiological recorder and is not heard by the nurses because they are too busy in the ward. This is a deception because the video monitors are being watched and if the child had an apnoeic attack, help could be summoned.
- The child is kept in the view of the cameras by being kept on or very near the bed by using physiological leads only 1.5 metres long. This is an inappropriate use of CVS, as the child is likely to have been fully investigated medically and physiological recordings will already have been done. The use of these leads is uncomfortable and restrictive for the child and is a further deception. The CVS protocol does not allow the child any free time outside the cubicle unattached to the equipment and away from the mother. Some have been observed continuously for 15 days. These circumstances are highly abnormal and stressful for both parent and child. The protocol for CVS should ensure they are both offered some respite.
- The mother is told that the child is being admitted for investigation of a serious problem: 'acute life-threatening events' or 'low oxygen levels' or 'apnoeic attacks' or similar phrases. This is very worrying for a mother who is inevitably likely to interpret this to mean that her child is seriously ill and at risk of dying or becoming brain damaged. Her reaction to this anxiety and to the stress of being in a cubicle with her child all day will add stress to the mother-child interaction. Any behaviour of a mother in these circumstances may reflect her stress and is unlikely to be indicative of how she would behave at home. Covert video recordings of the mother under these circumstances may therefore be highly abnormal and not represent how she has behaved at other times. It is important to realise

that there are no 'control' data about how mothers react in this situation.

- Before investigators decide to use CVS, they should consider what they will do if it proves negative. If the answer is that the child will still be taken into care, as reported in a letter in the British Medical Journal (Samuels and Southall, 1994) which said that 32 of 34 children subjected to CVS were taken into care, then CVS was probably unnecessary.

- It is reported that the diagnosis of MSBP is usually made at a median of 24 hours from the onset of CVS (Samuels and others, 1992). I find it surprising that a mother, whose child may not have had an 'apnoeic attack' for several weeks and has been investigated in hospital often for many days, would suffocate her child within a short time of being observed, unknown to her. I am concerned that there may have been times when the team interpreting the videos were over-zealous in what they consider to be attempted suffocation.

- CVS is undertaken specifically to witness the child being seriously harmed. If this does not happen, the videos should not be examined for any other possibly incriminating evidence.

- If videos are collected for evidence that may be used in court, then all the recordings of the mother and child should be exhibited to show how the mother cares for the child during the entire time. Any short episodes which may look suspicious should not be shown out of context. Video material which does not show evidence of abuse should not be erased (Samuels and Southall, 1994).

Concern about some investigations used to diagnose MSBP

Some of the investigative techniques used to diagnose MSBP are a cause for concern because they are not techniques accepted by the medical profession.

In a recent case, where a child was being investigated for apnoea, an electroencephalogram (EEG) was stated to show suffocation even though there was no recording of breathing patterns or oxygenation (Stephenson, 1994) and no video or eye witness record. EEG is not normally used in this way and cannot be used to diagnose suffocation.

In some cases where apnoeic attacks are being investigated, home event recording has been used (Poets and others, 1991). This records the baby's body movements and breathing patterns, skin oxygen levels and heart rate. Without an eye witness account, such recordings cannot be used to diagnose suffocation (Johnson and Morley, 1994). Abnormal recordings are much more likely to be due to natural events because they are so much more common than suffocation.

I am also concerned that some children have not had basic investigations. In a recent case, no blood tests had been performed even though the doctor said the child had been fully investigated. In several cases where the baby was considered to have acute life-threatening events, the throat had not been examined by an ear, nose and throat surgeon.

The apparent lack of compassion in some cases

I am concerned about how some of the mothers are treated. In one case, during the video a mother appeared to handle the baby roughly while trying to get her to suckle and the baby became very distressed. This lasted about 18 seconds. The baby did not become apnoeic, floppy or need resuscitation. Yet on the basis of this the police were called and arrested the mother. As far as I am aware, the paediatrician involved did not sit down with the mother and ask her what had happened in order to try to clarify what she had been doing. This goes against the grain of caring paediatric practice.

In conclusion

MSBP is a term that I suggest should be used with caution and preferably abandoned in favour of giving an exact description of what has happened to the child. It has become a diagnosis with emotional overtones which do not help in the management of these difficult cases. I do not consider that a mother exaggerating genuine symptoms or signs should be considered as a potential perpetrator of MSBP. I urge caution about some of the criteria for this diagnosis and concern about some of the accuracy, sensitivity and ethics of some techniques being used. I urge doctors to take detailed histories and talk to the mothers in a caring way about their concerns. It is important to protect a child who is being harmed by his or her mother. It is equally important not to harm the child by falsely accusing his or her mother of MSBP, thereby breaking up the family.

References

British Paediatric Association (February 1994) *Evaluation of suspected imposed upper airway obstruction,* Report of a working party, p.24, section 6.2.5

Clothier, C (1994) *The Report of the Allitt Inquiry.* HMSO

Johnson, P and Morley, C J (1994) 'Spying on mothers', *The Lancet*, 344, 132–133

Meadow, S R (1994) 'Who's to blame – mothers, Munchausen or medicine?, *Journal of the Royal College of Physicians*, 28, 332–337

Poets, C F, Samuels, M P, Noyes, J P, Jowes, J A, Southall, D P (1991) 'Home monitoring of transcutaneous oxygen tension in early detection of hypoxaemia in infant and young children', *Archives of Disease in Childhood*, 66, 676–682

Samuels, M P and Southall, D P (1992) 'Munchausen syndrome by proxy', *British Journal of Hospital Medicine*, 47(10), 759–762

Samuels, M P and Southall, D P (1994) 'Welfare of the child must come first', *British Medical Journal*, 308, 1101–1102

Samuels, M P, McClaughlin, W, Jacobsen, R, Poets, C F, Southall, D P (1992) 'Fourteen cases of imposed upper airway obstruction', *Archives of Disease in Childhood*, 67, 162–170

Stephenson, J P B (1994) 'Video surveillance in diagnosis of intentional suffocation', *The Lancet*, 344, 414–415

4. Nursing issues related to Munchausen syndrome by proxy

Chris Middleton, Senior Lecturer, Mid-Trent College of Nursing and Midwifery

Over the last 20 years children's nurses have been striving to create a philosophy of care which focuses on the needs of the child and family and within which children can be nursed in a way that will not unduly disrupt their daily routines or seriously affect their sensitive developmental processes. This philosophy of care has developed from a point of complete exclusion of a child's family during an admission to hospital, to one where parents and family members play a vital role in the care of their child. First came the recognition that a child is part of a family and the most important people in a child's life are his or her parents. They are, after all, the ones who carry out the bulk of his or her care, admission to hospital being usually only a very small 'blip' in his or her life career. Persistent lobbying by pressure groups such as Action for Sick Children made nurses, hospitals and doctors realise that children fared much better in hospital if their parents were more closely involved with their care during their stay. The changes necessary to encourage this involvement started with fairly basic concepts such as not restricting visiting, allowing parents to stay in hospital with their children and limiting a child's stay in hospital to the minimum necessary to achieve the medical aims. The next step was allowing parents to start to take on aspects of their child's daily nursing care, initially basic tasks such as feeding and washing.

The concept of family-centred care in children's nursing has grown out of an awareness of the need to develop a nursing care delivery programme that reflects a recognition of children's rights and the family's rights, duties and responsibilities with regard to their child. The importance of these issues has been emphasised by the implementation of the Children Act 1989 and the ratification of the 1989 United Nations Convention on the Rights of the Child.

The degree of involvement of the family has extended from basic care tasks to procedures of a more complex nature such as intravenous injections and naso-gastric feeding, but it should be noted that these procedures are only to be performed by parents after extensive training and assessment from the nursing staff. These developments are reflected in the Department of Health document (1991), *Welfare of Children and Young People in Hospital*. This document is mentioned in Recommendation 10 of the Allitt Inquiry report (see Appendix 1), where it is suggested that the Department of Health 'take steps to ensure that [it] is more closely observed'. Recommendation 10 is noteworthy also as being the only one whose content specifically relates to the nursing of sick children.

Paragraph 2.1 of the Department of Health guidance document reads:

'These basic principles inform all aspects of this guide

• Children are admitted to hospital only if the care they require cannot be as well provided at home, in a day clinic or on a day basis in hospital.

• Children requiring admission to hospital are provided with a high standard of medical, nursing and therapeutic care to facilitate a speedy recovery and minimise complications and mortality.

• Families with children have easy access to hospital facilities for children, without having to travel significantly further than to other similar amenities.

• Children are discharged from hospital as soon as socially and clinically appropriate and full support provided for subsequent home or day care.

• Good child health care is shared with parents/carers and they are closely involved in the care of their children at all times unless, exceptionally, this is not in the best interests of the child. Accommodation is provided for them to remain with their children overnight.

• Accommodation, facilities and staffing are appropriate to the needs of children and adolescents and separate from those provided for adults. Where possible separate accommodation is provided for adolescents.

• Like all other patients, children have the right for their privacy to be respected and to be treated with tact and understanding. They have an equal right to information appropriate to their age, understanding and specific circumstances.'

Family-centred care has also raised some issues for the current preparation of children's nurses. It has been necessary to incorporate a new philosophy into the nursing curriculum in this specialist area in order to meet the needs of a group of nurses who may spend a significant amount of their time in the role of expert teacher/supervisor of parents.

It is important to remember that these developments in children's nursing have not taken place in isolation to the developments in nursing generally. Advances in medicine and medical technology, a greater public awareness of what is possible and a greater willingness to complain when things are not right, are among the factors that have placed a pressure on nurses to develop a nursing service able to meet the demands of the 1990s and beyond. The response to this need has been to restructure the way that nursing care is delivered in order to exploit more fully the particular knowledge and expertise of nursing. The major advance in this respect is the introduction of a system of primary nursing, an approach to care delivery supported in the Patient's Charter (1991).

In simple terms, a system of primary nursing encourages the implementation of a patient-centred approach to nursing care. The primary nurse, who is considered an autonomous, expert practitioner, consults with and advises his or her allocated patients about their nursing care requirements. Among the advantages to the patient of this system, is the knowledge of a continuing relationship with one nurse during his or her stay in hospital or incapacity at home. For the nurse there is the satisfaction of 'being one's own boss'. The interpretation of a system of primary nursing within a family-centred care approach has created the opportunity for a nurse to take responsibility for the prescription of nursing care for a child during his or her admission or illness. For the care to be effective, there is a need for a close bond of trust and mutual respect to develop between the nurse, the patient and the family.

Fundamental to the philosophy of family-centred care is the desire and ability of the parents to take on the nursing care of their child, and the nurses will obviously do everything they can to support parents to care independently for their child. One of the warning signs, that Meadow (1977) proposed should alert staff to fabricated illness (MSBP), is the mother's greater anxiety about impressing the medical and nursing staff than about her child's illness. In family-centred care terms, therefore, what nurses may experience with MSBP is an 'ideal' parent: one who is approachable and friendly towards the nursing staff and about whom the nurses will find it difficult to have suspicions that she might be deliberately harming her own child. It is difficult to suspect someone you consider as a friend of something as terrible as child abuse, and to accuse someone falsely of such a crime has far-reaching implications for both the accuser and the accused, involving loss of trust and the destruction of the relationship. The combination of family-centred care and primary nursing may leave nurses working very closely with parents but becoming isolated from their professional colleagues with whom they would normally expect to share and discuss concerns. This will make suspicions of MSBP abuse even more difficult to deal with.

Many studies (Thornes, 1988; Department of Health, 1991; Audit Commission, 1991) have commented on the benefits of home care for children, an idea highlighted by the Platt Report (1959). However, the development of specific paediatric community nursing services has been slow and patchy, adversely affected by poor communication and inappropriate management arrangements. The often unclear management relationship between the paediatric community nurse, their directorate and the adult community nursing service, has left many children's community nurses functioning without proper support or clear guidance.

This lack of a satisfactory interface between primary and secondary care for children, with its concomitant poor communication, allows complex abusive behaviour such as found in MSBP to go largely unchecked or unchallenged. If, however, the GP and the primary health care team become the pivotal coordinators of care between specialists, then areas of concern can be shared between interested parties.

Consideration of MSBP creates many serious dilemmas for children's nurses. If, as the research suggests, some apparently kind and caring parents of sick children are the perpetrators of the child's 'sickness', then how are practitioners to know? Should we abandon all we have striven for in children's nursing for the last two decades and view every parent with suspicion for the sake of what may be a very rare situation, or should we continue with our policy of shared care and trust our experience (or gut feeling) to alert us to situations that should concern us? There are no easy answers to these questions, but a more child-focused system of care provision must surely help highlight areas of concern.

There may also be another issue for children's nurses when

faced with a conflict of interests between the needs of the family and the needs of the child. All nurses are professionally obliged to act in the best interests of their patient - to take the patient's part and act as advocate when the situation dictates. The children's nurse is also required to involve the family in the care. Is the nurse now bound to act always in the best interests of the child **and** family when the interests of each party are different, even contradictory, or do the interests of the child outweigh those of his or her family in such circumstances? For the registered nurse, advocacy is not an optional responsibility (UKCC, 1992) but it can be a double-edged sword. Representing – or speaking for – the patient may lead the nurse into conflict with others, who may, incidentally, think they also have the patient's best interests at heart.

Responding to Allitt

The publication of the Allitt Inquiry report (Clothier, 1994) has had serious implications for the delivery of health care for children, both in hospital and at home, and in particular for the recruitment, selection, training and employment of children's nurses. The high media profile afforded to the actions of nurse Beverley Allitt, who murdered children in her care, created a wave of public concern. Not unreasonably perhaps, there were many calls for an inquiry into the incidents in an attempt to establish how and when they occurred and to try and ensure that this situation could not be repeated again in any hospital ward in this country. The independent inquiry set up was chaired by Sir Cecil Clothier and heard evidence from various parties about the events that occurred on Ward Four at Grantham and Kesteven General Hospital between February and April 1991. The inquiry was heard in private and published its findings in early 1994. Included in the report are 12 recommendations (Appendix 1) arising from what the inquiry team describe as

'... lessons which should be heeded if every effort is to be made to contain such a catastrophe should it strike again'.

The inquiry team makes it clear in the report that the recommendations are not to be taken out of the context of the whole report. However, there have been allegations of almost bizarre policies and procedures being implemented in hospitals 'in light of Allitt'.

It is perhaps too easy to consider the Allitt Inquiry report as being a blueprint for policies to prevent serial killers from entering the nursing profession. This is not its function, however, and it is important to maintain the broader view offered within the report of how to ensure that when a nurse does start to cause a patient harm it can be detected before too much harm is done.

In an attempt to 'explain' Allitt's behaviour, much emphasis has been placed on a retrospective examination of her life. It was found that during her pre-nursing course she started to have frequent illnesses and injuries, none of which was considered particularly suspicious by staff at the time. Yet within the report this sickness record takes on more serious proportions and is offered, if it had been known at the time of her selection, as a reason not to have taken Allitt into nurse training. Although the consideration here would have officially been one of her reliability as an employee, a greater significance has become attached to all candidates' sickness records since the publication of the report. The extent to which the inquiry team felt that previous sickness patterns may indicate an unstable personality is demonstrated by the fact that concerns about candidates' sickness and absence occupy seven of their twelve recommendations. (See recommendations 1, 4, 5, 6, 7, 8 and 9 in the Appendix.)

This is an interesting development because the inquiry team appeared loathed to give Allitt a diagnosis. If the members were vague about reports of Allitt suffering from Munchausen syndrome (para 5.3), they were clear about their unwillingness to consider applying the 'by proxy' variation to her behaviour:

'Nor do we find the term Munchausen Syndrome By Proxy helpful in the context of our inquiry. . . . Furthermore, the application of an eponymous title runs the risk of implying unjustified certitude and of dignifying with a diagnostic label a horrific human deviance the origin and activation of which are totally beyond the comprehension of normal people.' (para 5.4.10)

But they did express concern about her mental status:

'... the causes of these attacks must be rooted in some form of mental instability ...' (para 5.2.1)

and this concern was further reflected in a document published in December 1994 offering guidance for occupational health services for National Health Service staff (HSG (94) 51). This guidance, while making it clear that no applicant should be refused employment on health grounds unless expert medical advice has been sought, also detailed the content of pre-employment health assessments:

'Particular attention should be paid to any applicant with a history of **excessive** sickness absence, **excessive** use of counselling or medical facilities, self-harming behaviour, or any other behaviour which may give cause for concern. . . . Rigid criteria used to assess 'personality disorders' are not thought to be of particular benefit because such diagnoses involve complex clinical judgements, taking into account all available evidence.' [my emphasis]

'Excessive' is not defined in this document. This may be a serious omission for those people who have made use of a counselling service prior to their entry into the nursing profession. The inquiry team themselves recognised that 'attention-seeking' behaviour may be a temporary phase in many young people's lives, yet they were willing to endorse a suggestion that use of these services should be sufficient reason to deny someone entry into nursing.

Consideration of the Allitt case raises very difficult questions about the provision of a safe nursing environment for children, especially within a hospital setting. The concept of safety here extends beyond considerations of security for vulnerable patients – an issue that has been highlighted by recent abductions of very young babies from hospital maternity units – and covers the supervision or monitoring of all who care for children. One of the reasons that Beverley Allitt was able to murder the children in her care for so long was that as a qualified member of staff she would have carried out most of her nursing care unobserved by others. Again we are left with a dilemma about the most appropriate way to react to this information. Should we now consider the constant monitoring of all members of staff in a children's ward in an attempt to prevent attacks occurring? And if we subscribe to this view, should this monitoring be **overt** and therefore possibly more of a deterrent or **covert,** thus providing us with evidence of someone actually committing a crime?

Covert video surveillance

Covert video surveillance (CVS) is a procedure that may be used when a child presents life-threatening symptoms that have not been explained satisfactorily. It involves the secret filming of a child and his or her close carer, usually the mother, during a period of hospital admission. The child is admitted to a specially prepared room which has a concealed video camera trained onto the child's bed or cot. The care interventions between child and carer are then filmed in order to confirm that the child's symptoms are due to some deliberate action on the part of the carer. If this is observed, the carer can then be confronted with 'irrefutable' evidence of their actions, and the video may also be used in a court as evidence to secure a criminal conviction.

CVS raises serious practice issues for nurses from both child protection and ethical perspectives. There is an ethical principle in health care, one that can be highlighted in all medical ethical codes from the Hippocratic Oath onwards, that underpins all health care endeavours. This principle is *beneficence* – the duty to do good and not to do harm.[1] Given this basic moral duty not to do harm, it is difficult, surely, for nurses and doctors to reconcile their role as a carer with the deliberate 'setting up' of a child to be harmed that is required with CVS.

However, beneficence is perhaps also concerned with minimising harm, and it could be argued that to expose the child to the short-term **harm** threatened by the use of CVS will ultimately lead to a longer-term **good** in the form of protection from the actions of the 'dangerous' carer. An analogy here might be surgery for the removal of an inflamed appendix: the operation is invasive and painful (short-term harm) but could be life-saving (longer-term good). The problem with this argument is that whereas appendicitis is unpredictable and an operation is usually the only possible option, in the case of children admitted for CVS there are already strong suspicions about the cause of their symptoms and there are other options available to secure their protection.

This is a complex point. While it may be right to argue from an ethical perspective against the use of CVS, in reality the protective policies and procedures in place for children about whose abuse there may be only 'strong suspicions' or 'reasonable doubt' are less than ideal. So in practice the desire of some practitioners to gain concrete, filmed evidence of abuse can be to some extent understood. The question now becomes how far are nurses, who are bound by their professional code to act as the child's advocate, prepared to accept the concept of the end justifying the means in these circumstances? Surely, if nurses are truly to 'speak for the child', they must insist on the end being achieved by some other means, ones that do not expose their charge to any unnecessary or foreseeable risk of harm.

However, the argument should not be seen as a choice between two options: acceptance of CVS **or** invoking less than perfect child protection policies.

---

1   Some moral philosophers may distinguish between the moral principles of beneficence and non maleficence, but for our purposes we will consider both doing good and not doing harm under the common principle of beneficence.

'CVS is an example of the perceived need for evidence outweighing good child protection procedures, and the fair treatment of families and children.' (Thomas, 1994)

The issue of CVS should not steer us away from the refining of child protection procedures and identification of good practice that has been developing following the recommendations made in various inquiry reports. A number of these reports, including the Cleveland Inquiry report (1988), have made specific recommendations about the partnership between parents and the child protection agencies. The Cleveland Inquiry report, for example, recommends that parents should be involved, given information and 'helped to understand the steps that are being taken'. This philosophy underpins the concept of family-centred care in nursing.

The courts, recognising the importance of promoting a coherent strategy for dealing with cases of child abuse, have not looked kindly on instances where the advice from the inquiries has been ignored (see *Re: E (A Minor) (Child abuse: evidence* (1991) 1 FLR 420). This openness in dealing with parents extends to the easier access to personal files and medical records - both the subject of statutory powers - and the greater involvement of parents in child protection case conferences.

The underlying principle of the 1989 Children Act and the 1989 UN Convention on the Rights of the Child and all child protection policies and procedures, is that of the centrality of the best interests of the child. This immediately begs the question of whether the deceit of CVS to entrap the parents is in the best interests of the child.

If CVS is to be used as a child protection tool, then there is a need to ensure that all other avenues to achieve the safety of the child have been explored before admission to hospital for the purposes of surveillance (British Paediatric Association, 1994).

CVS in its present form is being used to monitor the activities of parents. However, there may be moves, 'in light of Allitt', to extend this secret surveillance to include all the staff on a children's ward. This may be introduced under the guise of improving security. The acceptability of this for hospital staff is difficult to determine. Delegates at a recent conference, when this question was posed to them, were divided in their responses. Legally, the situation is unclear: there does not appear to be any absolute right to privacy - certainly an issue for people in the public eye; equally, we are all under surveillance from security cameras in shops, banks and shopping malls, and in some towns and cities there are surveillance cameras on the streets. Video camera surveillance of traffic movement has also been part of our environment for some time. We have grown to accept all of these instances. Yet the concept of being secretly watched while we work provokes feelings of moral indignation in most people.

There are important points to be made here. Most of the videoing that we encounter in our daily lives is overt - we can see the cameras, we know what is happening and we can choose whether or not we want to participate. Unlike CVS, it is not secret and it is to some extent a consensual activity. The obvious nature of these methods strengthens their role as crime deterrents, but crime still occurs even when these cameras are present, and it is likely that those who, like Allitt, wish to perpetrate their particular crimes will do so in spite of any surveillance method.

It should be pointed out that the Allitt Inquiry report does not mention the use of strategies such as CVS. In fact it only makes simple recommendations about improving practice and stricter adherence to existing and accepted policies and procedures:

> 'No single circumstance or individual can be held responsible for what happened. But taken together, the catalogue of lapses from the high standards to which the National Health Service aspires point to lessons which should be heeded if every effort is to be made to contain such a catastrophe should it strike again.'

These lessons are not new, however. A study reported in The New England Journal of Medicine (Buehler and others, 1985) investigated an unusual increase in the mortality rate for patients on the cardiology ward of a children's hospital. Allegations had been made about one of the nursing staff with regard to irregularities in the administration of a drug to many of the children who died, although nothing was ever proved. One of the report's conclusions was:

> 'Although no hospital is immune to the possible misuse of medicines by employees, improved control and documentation should discourage such acts.'

Conclusion

In many ways the issues for nurses arising from Allitt's actions and Munchausen syndrome by proxy abuse are similar. Both are concerned with something extraordinary, and they thrive on malcommunication and lack of exploration of the unusual. One could expect, therefore, that the responses will be similar. It may be that the main lesson from the Allitt Inquiry, that of heightening awareness 'of the possibility of malevolent intervention as a cause of unexplained clinical events', could also serve as an appropriate response to the issue of MSBP abuse.

The last word here belongs to the Allitt Inquiry, from the Epilogue:

> 'Civilised society has very little defence against the aimless malice of a deranged mind. . . . The tightening of standards which we have sometimes urged must be a good in itself and such small improvements may reduce the opportunities open to another Beverley Allitt.'

References

Audit Commisson (1991) *Measuring Quality: The patient's view of day surgery.* NHS occasional papers No.3, HMSO

British Paediatric Association (1994) *Evaluation of suspected imposed upper airway obstruction.* Report of a working party

Buehler, J and others (1985) 'Unexplained deaths in a children's hospital', *The New England Journal of Medicine*, 313, 4, 211-216

Clothier, C (1994) *The Report of the Allitt Inquiry.* HMSO

Department of Health (1991) *The Patient's Charter.* HMSO

Department of Health (1991) *Welfare of Children and Young People in Hospital.* HMSO

HSG (94) 51 Guidance re: Occupational Health Services for NHS Staff issued by the NHS Executive 6 December 1994

Meadow, S R (1977) 'Munchausen syndrome by proxy: the hinterland of child abuse', *The Lancet* ii, 343-345

Meadow, S R (1982) 'Munchausen syndrome by proxy', *Archives of Disease in Childhood*, 57, 92-98

Platt Report (1959) *The Welfare of Children in Hospital.* Ministry of Health, HMSO

The Report of the Inquiry into Child Abuse in Cleveland 1987. HMSO (1988)

Thomas, T (1994) 'Covert video surveillance in child protection work', *Family Law*, September, 524-526

Thornes, R *(1988) Hidden children: An analysis of ward attenders in children's wards.* NAWCH (now Action For Sick Children)

UKCC (United Kingdom Central Council for Nursing, Midwifery and Health Visiting) (1992) *Code of Professional Conduct* 3rd Edition

Appendix
The Allitt Inquiry Report Recommendations

1 **We recommend** that, for all those seeking entry to the nursing profession, in addition to routine references the most recent employer or place of study should be asked to provide at least a record of time taken off on grounds of sickness (para 2.4.4).

2 **We recommend** that in every case Coroners should send copies of post mortem reports to any consultant who has been involved in the patient's care prior to death whether or not demanded under rule 57 of the Coroner's Rules 1984 (para 4.2.9).

3 **We recommend** that the provision of paediatric pathology services be reviewed with a view to ensuring that such services be engaged in every case in which the death of a child is unexpected or clinically unaccountable, whether the post mortem examination is ordered by a Coroner or in routine hospital practice (para 4.2.16).

4 **We recommend** that no candidate for nursing in whom there is evidence of major personality disorder should be employed in the profession (para 5.4.11).

5 **We recommend** that nurses should undergo formal health screening when they obtain their first posts after qualifying (para 5.5.13). We acknowledge that in Allitt's case this was done.

6 **We recommend** that the possibility be reviewed of making available to Occupational Health departments any records of absence through sickness from any institution which an applicant for a nursing post has attended or been employed by (para 5.5.14).

7 **We recommend** that procedures for management referrals to Occupational Health should make clear the criteria which should trigger such referrals (para 5.5.14).

8 **We recommend** that further consideration be given to how the suggestion of the Chairman of the Association of NHS Occupational Health Physicians (see para 5.5.16) could be applied in practice (para 5.5.17).

9 **We recommend** that consideration be given to how General Practitioners might, with the candidate's consent, be asked to certify that there is nothing in the medical history of a candidate for employment in the National Health Service which would make then unsuitable for their chosen occupation (para 5.5.19).

10 **We recommend** that the Department of Health should take steps to ensure that its guide, *Welfare of Children and Young People in Hospital*, is more closely observed (para 5.8.8).

11 **We recommend** that in the event of failure of an alarm on monitoring equipment, an untoward incident report should be completed and the equipment serviced before it is used again (para 5.11.6).

12 **We recommend** that reports of serious untoward incidents to District and Regional Health Authorities should be made in writing and through a single channel which is known to all involved (para 5.14.12).

5. Munchausen syndrome by proxy and risk assessment: a recipe for dangerous practice

Jan Horwath, Child Care Training Manager and Lecturer, University of Sheffield, in consultation with Margaret Kessel, Social Worker, Children's Hospital, Sheffield

Introduction

Historically, those working in the area of child abuse confront society with the reality that parents can physically injure, sexually abuse, emotionally harm and neglect their children. As each form of child abuse is 'discovered', it seems that a process is followed whereby there is an initial resistance by society to believing parents could do such things to their children – as evidence is offered there is a response of anger and indignation and a reluctant acceptance – before an acknowledgement of a need to respond and act to protect children from this abuse, while not implicating innocent parents. The tension around responding to and balancing children's and parents' rights underpins the investigative process in child protection and can impair objective risk assessment. This occurs because individuals working with child abuse approach situations with their own values, attitudes and previous experiences, as well as a perception of the norms and standards of society. This has been well documented in other publications (Redar, Duncan and Gray, 1993). Kempe and others (1980), in a paper exploring the 'unrecognised trauma' of the battered child syndrome concluded:

> 'Physicians, because of their own feelings and their difficulty in playing a role that they find hard to assume, may have great reluctance in believing that parents were guilty of abuse. They may find it difficult to initiate a proper investigation so as to assure adequate management

of the case. Above all, the physician's duty and responsibility to the child requires a full evaluation of the problem and a guarantee that the expected repetition of trauma will not be permitted to occur.'

Their summary encapsulates the dilemmas faced, not only by doctors, but by all professionals involved in assessments of potential cases of Munchausen syndrome by proxy (MSBP).

This chapter examines the way in which professionals make assessments and the dangerous practice that can occur as those working with potential cases of MSBP come to terms with or resist acknowledging, accepting and responding to this form of child abuse. It is based on discussions with professions involved in cases of MSBP. We are aware that when analysing responses to situations and reflecting on them with the benefit of hindsight, it is easy to make assessments about dangerous practice that were not apparent at the time. Our intention is not to criticise individual bad practice but to highlight some of the problematic areas of risk assessment in potential cases of MSBP, and to offer guidance to professionals who may currently or in the future be involved in such situations.

A child protection assessment involves collating signs and indicators that a child is potentially being abused. In cases of physical abuse there may be medical evidence to indicate non-accidental injury. Although MSBP is categorised as a form of physical abuse, the indicators are often not overtly apparent and the investigative and assessment process can be very complex; professionals usually initially believe that they have a child who is ill through organic causes and a mother who is concerned and anxious. Our experience of MSBP and the experiences outlined in this book, indicate that some of the problems surrounding an assessment of MSBP focus on the subjectivity introduced into the assessment process by the professionals involved. This subjectivity can occur at two levels. The first involves the individual professional and his or her response to a mother who may be exhibiting the behaviour patterns labelled as MSBP. The second focuses on the way in which professionals interact with each other and the family involved during the assessment process.

Images of motherhood and the impact on the assessment process

In possible cases of MSBP professionals may have to confront and challenge the dominant view of motherhood. 'The power of the mother and child Madonna image appears to be strong in most cultures and traditions, the concept of mothering appears to be one

of the universals of humankind.' (Pugh, De'Ath ar.
Professionals are faced with looking beyond this
the caring and nurturing mother to someone who
inducing or fabricating illness in her child to gain
herself.

They can respond in a variety of ways. One of the most common responses is that of denial; for example, believing a sensitive mother cannot possibly be interfering with the feeds of her child. In one case, the hospital consultant approached the general practitioner to share his opinion that this was a possible case of MSBP. The general practitioner refused to accept this; he was a friend of the family and was insistent that the mother could not behave in this way. Despite being given evidence to indicate the mother was poisoning the child, the general practitioner was convinced the child had an unusual allergy and had referred the child to an alternative therapy centre.

This example also highlights the way in which professionals can become over-involved when working with possible perpetrators of MSBP. The carer is frequently friendly, helpful and affectionate towards staff, sending them birthday cards, and showing interest in their personal lives. This can result in the professional losing clarity between their professional assessment of the carer and their personal feelings towards them as individuals. In Chapter 8 of this book, Fox describes the impact this can have. Referring to a mother he writes,

> 'There is no doubt that a lot of staff were intimidated by her, yet with others she formed a close relationship, the effect being that at ward meetings the staff were completely divided about her and professional objective judgements were clouded.'

Professionals can make assumptions about the 'natural love' a carer has for his or her child, preventing him or her from abusing the child. Dingwell and others (1983) describe this phenomenon and the impact it can have on risk assessment. In potential cases of MSBP, professionals can use the notion of 'mother love' as a way of avoiding having to contemplate the possibility that the mother may be subjecting the child to unnecessary medical procedures. Comments we have heard include, 'But she's the mother, she couldn't possibly do that to her own child' 'She is such a devoted parent, how could you think that of her?' 'It's not natural – no mother could do that to her own child'.

This defence mechanism highlights the struggle to accept that a mother may not fit our stereotypical image of motherhood. Perceptions can be confused by the mixed messages given by these others. They present as caring, concerned and committed to their children; rarely are there specific overt indicators that may alert one to abusive behaviour. This is clearly described by a social worker who received a referral to support a mother whose child was having life-threatening attacks. No sooner had the child recovered and was due for discharge, than another attack occurred. The doctors were puzzled and the mother distraught. She was desperate for the doctors to find some way of saving her child. The social worker felt despair and sympathy as she comforted the weeping and sobbing mother. The worker had considered MSBP, but seeing the mother in this state, she felt guilty that she could possibly have misjudged her. It was only when the mother herself was admitted to hospital that the attacks stopped. Empty capsules of a sedative were found in her possession and when the child was tested, the drug was found in his bloodstream. This left the worker feeling vulnerable and full of professional self-doubt. She felt angry with herself for empathising with the mother and felt guilty for being partially responsible for the suffering of the child. The assessment had become subjective, as the focus moved away from the child to the parent and the primary concerns of the worker were about the way the parent felt. Another social worker described how she suspected MSBP but 'the thought of suggesting this when a mother may really have a very sick child seemed so awful. I could not do it.' The focus had shifted from child-centred to parent-centred, the child protection issues and the possible suffering of the child becoming a secondary consideration.

Manifestations of dangerousness in practice

Professionals can make subjective assessments as they become dominated by a fixed idea. Those who argue that MSBP does not exist, state that doctors frequently make a diagnosis of MSBP and refuse to look for alternative organic causes, convinced they have made a correct diagnosis. Our experience is the complete opposite: that paediatricians are so concerned about missing a rare organic cause to explain the illness of the child that they do not consider an alternative explanation and instead subject the child to a whole range of painful tests and exploratory surgery. One doctor was not prepared to consider the possibility that the mother could be inducing illness in the child, despite consistent evidence that when the mother herself was in hospital the health of the child improved. The doctor said he would feel foolish if he missed a rare organic disorder and continued medical investigations on the child, ignoring the possibility of any other explanation for the child's illness.

Dingwall and others (1983) describe the 'rule of optimism' as the process by which professionals always think the best of the parents. This is very easy to do in suspected cases of MSBP, as the mother presents as a devoted carer whose attention appears to be focused on meeting the needs of her child. Faced with this situation, in contrast to other situations of child abuse where negative interactions may be observed, it is easy to focus on the good mother and ignore any indicators that may contradict our perceptions. In one case of MSBP, for example, a health visitor noted that the child drew away when the mother tried feeding her with a spoon. The health visitor presumed this was the child associating spoon-feeding with medicine, not considering, despite many other indicators, that there was another reason. In fact the child was being administered poison in this way.

In an attempt to avoid being faced with acknowledging that a mother may be fabricating or inducing illness in a child, professionals may subconsciously ignore or fail to report certain pieces of information. One example of this was in a case where the mother had given a medical history for the child. The staff nurse also spoke to the father and noted that some of the information did not correlate with the account from the mother. The nurse presumed the father had got confused and did not record the disparities. It was only weeks later when MSBP was on the agenda that the nurse recalled the conversations and realised the relevance.

Another common situation is information not being cross referenced. This can happen when the child is taken to different hospitals and clinics. One example of this was a situation involving a boy aged 11 months. The social worker discovered the child had been taken by his mother to two different hospitals on 11 occasions over an eight-month period. Medical staff had not linked the involvement of the other hospital and were concerned that they were missing a rare disease, unaware that the presentations at the other hospital were with very different symptoms.

Professionals can also collude with mothers in cases of MSBP: if the mother develops a good relationship with a worker and confides in them, the worker may not appreciate the way in which they are being influenced by a mother. For example, a mother who presents a desperate and anxious picture about her child may exaggerate the symptoms: say the temperature is higher that it is, or the child ate less than they did. A worker may witness this but rationalise the behaviour of the mother, arguing to themselves that the mother is keen to get help for her child.

One of the problems in making an assessment of MSBP is that

the condition is very rare, particularly in its life-threatening form. A professional may only be faced with a small number of cases in their whole career. It is therefore understandable that professionals focus purely on organic causes. The rarity of these situations can result in professionals becoming immobilised by the implications of the MSBP label and avoiding making decisions. In one case, for example, the paediatrician suspected MSBP but discharged the child, making a referral to the social worker to follow up, as they could think of no alternative course of action. The social worker visited the next day, to find the child had already been taken by the mother to another hospital. In another case described by Fox in this book, a manager at a social services department refused to consider the case as a child protection referral, despite the death of a sibling, referrals from the paediatrician that he suspected MSBP and a statement from the father that the mother was starving the children.

We have noted that those working in the area of child protection are confused by the label 'MSBP'. There is very little understanding of what MSBP is and how it manifests itself. Frequently professionals on training courses have commented that MSBP is 'what Beverley Allitt had' and they need not pay much attention to the syndrome in terms of abuse by parents, as perpetrators tend to be care staff. The consequence of this is that information or even a referral is not treated appropriately. A classic example of this is noted by Fox, who reports a case of a social worker recording the child 'had Munchausen Disease, as if it was a physical condition like measles'. One of the problems can be that workers feel too intimidated by other professionals actually to state that they do not understand what MSBP is describing and try instead to guess at its meaning.

In suspected cases of MSBP, it is crucial that the accuracy of information, particularly that received from the mother, is checked. MSBP highlights the dangers that can occur when guidelines and procedures are followed and recordings made without considering why this needs to be done. For example, temperature, feeding and urine charts are routine parts of hospital procedures, but in some situations the focus is on checking they are completed rather than who completed them and the accuracy of information recorded. In some cases it has been difficult to establish whether the carer recorded inaccurate information or tampered with the charts, as the charts are handwritten and completed by a variety of personnel.

The role of the supervisor

The Survey of Inquiry Reports (Department of Health, 1991) noted,

'Inquiry reports tend to underestimate the impact of clients on professionals. Recognition is needed not only of the conflicts and problems within professional interaction but also between professionals, parents and children.'

These effects are often not recognised by professionals:

'Workers (not just social workers) are easily drawn into collusive relationships not out of ignorance or perversity, but because of their response to pain, and their guilt at not being able to prevent this.'

In view of this fact, it is important that workers have an opportunity to discuss their work. The impact of the client and their carers on the worker needs to be acknowledged and considered as an integral part of the assessment process.

'For supervisors, it is important to tune into often unspoken feelings in order to help the worker clarify whose interests are being serviced by proposed action or inactivity.' (Richards, Payne and Shepperd, 1990)

However, many professionals involved in potential cases of MSBP do not receive the kind of supervision that would enable them to explore the unhealthy processes that can operate when working with clients. Many professionals receive supervision that focuses on the management task, considering workload and budget priorities. Some professionals – consultants, for example – receive no supervision regarding cases, which may result in some of the processes outlined above remaining unchallenged. A case was described to us of a consultant paediatrician who refused to consider the possibility that the case with which he was dealing might be MSBP. It was just after the Allitt case had received much publicity and his view was that his medical team were obsessed by MSBP. Some of the personnel were so concerned at what they felt were clear indicators of MSBP being ignored, that they approached another consultant, who agreed that MSBP should be considered but felt it would be unethical to discuss this with the first consultant, unless they requested a consultation themselves.

When supervision is available, it does not necessarily mean that objective risk assessments will take place. Processes can go on in supervision that distort the assessment process. The supervisor may have as much difficulty as the worker coping with the stress of child protection work and the implications of MSBP and may well mirror, in the supervisory relationship, the unconscious process that operates between worker and client. An example of this is a case involving a health visitor who had difficulty accepting that a mother was fabricating illness in her child. The mother insisted the child had asthma attacks, despite having no evidence, and there were conflicting reports of these attacks between mother and father. The health visitor believed the mother, choosing to ignore and not record her discussions with the father. The health visitor discussed the case with the supervisor, who had a lot of respect for the worker and accepted what she said, in spite of conflicting reports from another health visitor who had also visited the family.

A number of front-line staff who have suspected cases of MSBP, have discussed MSBP as a possibility with their supervisors and have met with the same diversity of responses as have been found among professionals. There are dangers when supervisors dismiss or ignore these assessments: the Professional Accommodation Syndrome (Morrison, 1993) can take effect.

Morrison examined the Accommodation Syndrome which Summit (1983) used as a model to describe ways in which children who have been sexually abused learn to accommodate the abuse. Morrison felt that professionals can mirror this process in the way in which they manage stressful child protection cases. The process has five stages:

- secrecy;
- helplessness;
- entrapment or accommodation;
- delayed disclosure;
- retraction.

It operates in the following way. A nurse, for example, is concerned about the way a mother is behaving on the ward. She suspects the mother may be interfering with the drip set up for the child, but has no proof. She tries telling the charge nurse, who dismisses the suggestion. She then feels foolish and keeps her thoughts secret. She observes the behaviour of the mother and has more concerns, but feels she had better not say anything, so she feels helpless and begins to 'accommodate' her concerns. She rationalises what she sees, thinking that the mother must be so concerned for her child that she is constantly checking the drips are right and is being over-protective. The nurse may then witness some more behaviour which makes her think her initial concerns were justified. She may go back to the charge nurse or try telling the paediatrician. The response may again be to dismiss what is said, or to respond, for example by confronting the mother. If the nurse is made to feel she cannot cope with the consequences of these actions – for example, if the mother is devastated by the confrontation – the nurse may retract what she said and once again accommodate her concerns. In our opinion, the more powerful the person to whom the worker discloses and the more negative the response, the more likely it is that the worker will keep their opinions secret. One nurse described how she tentatively suggested to a paediatrician during a ward round that this could possibly be a case of MSBP, substantiating her reasons for thinking this. The doctor laughed and told her not to be foolish. The nurse felt unable to share further concerns with her ward sister, as she had laughed with the doctor. A social worker tried sharing her concerns with her manager and was dismissed with 'you would think that, wouldn't you?' The worker felt so intimidated that she was unable to argue her case further.

The role of the supervisor in risk assessment and MSBP is crucial and covers a number of areas which can be linked to the supervisory tasks of management, development, support and mediation. As a manager, the supervisor should ensure that the supervisee has an appropriate workload, enabling them to complete the required tasks. One task frequently given little priority is that of recording, which can be crucial in cases of MSBP. Frequently, records in MSBP cases describe an incident such as a child having a fit, but with little additional information – who witnessed it, who reported it – information that is crucial in assessing possible cases of MSBP. Recording is often handwritten with no signature, making it difficult to clarify if information is not clear.

The supervisor also has a role in developing the skills of the supervisees. In cases of child protection, this should involve ensuring staff are aware of signs and indicators of abuse, child protection guidelines and procedures, and their individual specific roles and responsibilities. Discussion and debate should be ongoing, the focus being to give the supervisee the opportunity of developing good practice. It may be that the supervisee is sent on training courses to cover areas described above. If this is the case, the supervisor has a responsibility to ensure that the worker has an opportunity to reflect on and consider the practical implications of their learning. They then require an opportunity to put the learning into practice and reflect on their experiences. Within this framework, possible cases of MSBP could be discussed and monitored. The role of the supervisor is to ensure the focus is child-centred and the worker is aware of the child protection context and their role and responsibilities.

The supervisor also needs to support the worker and be aware of the unhealthy process that can operate when a worker is involved in stressful child protection cases. The supervisor has a responsibility to challenge these processes while recognising the impact this work can have on staff. The worker should feel supported and able to approach the supervisor to debrief and share their feelings and anxieties in a way that feels safe and secure and should ultimately ensure an objective risk assessment.

The supervisor has a role as a mediator and can facilitate communication with other professional groups, particularly if the worker feels intimated as described above.

Finally, the supervisor needs to have supervision in their own right so they, in turn, have the opportunity to explore the way their behaviour may be impacting on the work and ultimately the child.

Professional collaboration and the assessment process

Assessments are not dependent on one individual but involve a number of professionals from different backgrounds. The objectivity of the assessment will therefore be determined by the way that these professionals work together. Power dynamics have a crucial part to play in the way in which professionals relate to each other when making joint risk assessments. One of the ways this can manifest itself is in what Reder, Duncan and Gray (1993) describe as the 'exaggeration of hierarchy'. This occurs when certain professionals are perceived as being powerful, while other workers feel intimidated and are afraid to challenge their opinions. We have described how this can occur on a one-to-one basis but it can have more impact on risk assessment if a group of professionals are involved. In one case of suspected MSBP, both the consultant paediatrician and the social work manager were sceptical that they were in fact dealing with a case of MSBP and wanted to continue looking for organic causes. The junior sister, staff nurse and night staff, the social worker and health visitor all felt there was sufficient evidence to consider the possibility of MSBP, but felt unable to argue against a consultant and a social work manager. The result in this case was that the child was discharged from hospital, only to be readmitted with a serious overdose of sleeping tablets the following day.

In other situations professionals can be divided in their assessment and hold polarised views. For example, at one case conference consideration was being given to the future of a second child, born to a mother who was felt to have MSBP (her first child had been removed from her care after innumerable unnecessary medical interventions). Representatives from the medical team were adamant that the second child was at risk. Representatives from social services argued that the mother should keep the child but with close supervision. The focus of the conference moved from assessing the needs of the child and the degree of risk, to challenging the perceptions of the different professionals. The medical team felt the social workers were behaving like 'wishy washy liberals' while the social work team felt the medics were 'authoritarian and unfeeling'. In this case, the views became more polarised and entrenched as those involved felt the need to demonstrate that their professional perspective was appropriate. It was only when the social services department decided to apply for a supervision order that a guardian ad litem was appointed, who moved the focus back onto the needs of the child.

MSBP focuses to a considerable degree on medical assessments and it is inevitable that they will dominate the process. However, the medical team can sometimes become unable to consider that the illness of a child may not have an organic cause and consequently do not involve other professionals until the child may have been subjected to many unnecessary medical tests. Preconceived views of the ways in which professionals operate can often result in a reluctance to involve the appropriate agencies. One of the common features of many of the cases described in this book is the reluctance of medical personnel to involve the police until all other alternatives have been considered. The stereotypical image of the police can result in medical staff fearing an insensitive intervention, which would upset the family and disrupt the ward. In these situations, police are rarely consulted as to how they would approach the situation. Instead, the medical staff base their opinions on previous experiences or their own assumptions.

MSBP is an area of child protection where there can be confusion over roles. As the focus is particularly on medical intervention, the child protection issues can become lost, the medical personnel feeling that they are responsible for making an assessment without involving the child protection investigating agencies. Schreier and Libow (1993) quote from two American paediatricians who vividly describe their confusion.

'As a physician one of the things you learn early on is to listen to the parents. And what makes Munchausen syndrome by proxy so difficult to deal with is that your ally in the child's health care is really not your ally. I don't want to use the word 'adversary', but in fact I guess it is an adversarial relationship, because they are playing a game with you, except you don't know you're playing a game.'

'Frankly, I'm not a detective. I'm not Perry Mason and I don't want to be. It's difficult enough to accuse somebody, but for me to have to start snooping around and becoming a detective, and looking through drawers – I don't want to do that. That's not my role....And I think that makes it even more difficult because when you finally accuse the person, it's a question of, 'Well can you prove it?' Well no, I can't prove it.... If they are looking for hard evidence, it's not going to be there. I'm not going to find a bottle of Milk of Magnesia in the mother's purse with her fingerprints on it, and I'm not going to put a hidden camera or a hidden microphone in a room to try to catch the person....And the thought of putting cameras in rooms and trying to catch people is repugnant to me. We seek alliances with parents, not adversarial relationships.' (Thoughts of a paediatric gastroenterologist on experiences with Munchausen syndrome by proxy cases)

'No I didn't have a whole lot of doubt about being wrong. I just didn't know how to accuse the mother or confront the needs of the child given that she was sort of between me and the kid. I should have, in retrospect. I should have called the social worker and said 'You know, something weird is going on'. Because we were all convinced of it. We had these hallway, stairwell, and elevator conversations. I remember vividly how we all decided that she was crazy.' (Retrospective thoughts of a physician about a mother with several children who died in suspicious circumstances)

In both these examples the paediatricians demonstrate some confusion regarding the boundary of their role and that of the investigating agencies, police and social worker. They appear to be rationalising their lack of action by stating it is not part of their role, rather than referring to those who clearly have an investigatory role.

Strategies to promote objective assessments

Gray, Bentovim and Milla, in Chapter 11 of this book, highlight that the successful management of initial suspicion and identification is dependent on the team being alert to the possibility of illness being induced in children and recommend that suspicions are shared in a multi-disciplinary arena. The guidance on child protection and medical responsibilities produced by the Department of Health (1995) is particularly useful, as it emphasises the importance of preliminary discussion among professionals when 'child abuse is a consideration'. It also emphasises that this is not the beginning of an investigation and there may be 'a degree of tentativeness about the information'. This approach would facilitate a child protection-focused examination of information at an early stage where MSBP may be a concern but it can only take place if professionals are prepared to trust and communicate honestly with each other. This can happen if efforts are made to break down inter-agency barriers through inter-agency training and networking.

'The value of multi-disciplinary training is that it extends the knowledge base, enables participants to understand and appreciate the skills of others, increases understanding of professional roles and leads to a better understanding of the problems faced by other professional groups. Multi-disciplinary training will also promote the development of realistic joint working procedures based on a thorough knowledge and appreciation of the skills other disciplines possess and the difficulties faced in putting these skills into practice.' (Department of Health, 1995)

Training that takes place in a local context can break down barriers that exist between professionals and can facilitate better working relationships, dispelling many of the stereotypical images professionals have of each other. Evaluations following inter-agency training events frequently include comments from participants about feeling more confident in approaching other professionals, as they have met them and had an opportunity to discuss child protection practice. The development of locally-based guidelines and procedures regarding MSBP can also promote appropriate arrangements for working together. Professionals have more confidence in contacting colleagues if they have an agreed framework within which to operate.

Conclusion

Risk assessment is complex in any child protection situation and the professional is always anxious about misjudging and making the wrong decision. As we are dealing with human beings who behave in unpredictable ways, it will never be possible to make decisions that we know are one hundred per cent accurate. However, we owe it to the children we work with to ensure that our assessments are as objective as they can be. This can only happen if individuals are prepared to examine their own practice and if professionals communicate honestly and effectively with each other in an environment that promotes trust and positive working relationships.

References

Department of Health (1991) *Child Abuse: Study of Inquiry Reports 1980–89*. HMSO

Department of Health (1995) *Child Protection: Medical Responsibilities*. British Medical Association and Conference of Medical Royal Colleges

Dingwall, R, Eekelarr, J M, Murray, T (1983) *The Protection of Children: state intervention and family life*. Blackwell

Kempe, C H and others (1980) 'The Battered Child Syndrome' *in* Cooke, J and Boules, R (eds) *Child Abuse Commission and Omission*. Butterworth

Morrison, T (1993) *Staff Supervision in Social Care*. Longman

Pugh, G, De'Ath, E, Smith, C (1994) *Confident Parents, Confident Children: policy and practice in parent education and support*. National Children's Bureau

Reder, P, Duncan, S, Gray, M (1993) *Beyond Blame: child abuse tragedies revisited*. Routledge

Richards, M, Payne, C, Shepperd, A (1990) *Staff Supervision in Child Protection Work*. National Institute of Social Work

Schreier, H A and Libow, J A (1993) *Hurting for Love (Munchausen by proxy syndrome)*. Guildford Press

Summit, R (1983) 'The Child Sexual Abuse Accommodation Syndrome', *Child Abuse and Neglect*, 7 (2)

6.   The use of covert video surveillance: an inter-agency approach

Sandra Shaw, Operations Manager, Staffordshire Social Services

Introduction

Munchausen's syndrome by proxy is a description of a type of abuse that is used for some children who have been abused by their adult carers. Providing evidence that this type of abuse has occurred has proved difficult, yet its consequence for these children is grave.

The use of covert video surveillance (CVS) to demonstrate how some children had suffered abuse was developed by paediatricians in Staffordshire. Its use, however, needed to be placed within inter-agency child protection procedures. In order to achieve this, representatives of statutory agencies worked to produce a protocol governing the use of CVS. The development of this protocol took many hours of discussion, reflection and work on the part of social work managers, paediatricians, senior nursing staff, lawyers, hospital managers and senior police officers. An initial position of lack of inter-agency agreement on the use of CVS moved in the course of nine months to a protocol that was owned by all agencies involved in its drafting, approved by the Staffordshire Area Child Protection Committee, supported by the Department of Health and accepted by the Association of Directors of Social Services and Association of Chief Police Officers.

It is fair to acknowledge that there were times of agreement and disagreement. The range of emotions, professional sensitivities and professional judgements, which are commonplace in inter-agency work, were evident in the drafting of the protocol. This was heightened by the fact that agencies were dealing with the crucial issue of protecting young vulnerable children from physical harm. In addition, the use of CVS raised questions for professional philosophies and practices, and legal consequences for the hospital and the County Council if any neglect or flaw were found in the procedure. The use of CVS, however, is not an unlawful procedure in itself.

Protecting children

The duties to protect children are clear. The United Nations Convention on the Rights of the Child which was ratified by the United Kingdom Government on 16 December 1991 and accepted by Staffordshire Social Services Committee as underpinning their Children's Services Strategy in January 1993, states:

> 'In all actions concerning children, whether undertaken by public or private social welfare institutions, Courts of law, administrative authorities or legislative bodies the best interests of the child should be a primary consideration. State parties undertake to ensure the child such protection and care as is necessary for his or her wellbeing taking into account the rights and duties of his/her parents, guardians or other individuals legally responsible for him or her and to this end take all appropriate legislative and administrative measures.'

The *Principles and Practice in Regulations and Guidance* (Department of Health, 1990b) published following the passing of the Children Act 1989 (Department of Health, 1990a) state clearly that children are entitled to protection from neglect, abuse and exploitation; the Children Act lays specific responsibility on local authorities to prevent children within their own areas suffering ill treatment and neglect. The Act also enshrines the principle that the child's welfare shall be the court's paramount consideration. Sections 17 and 47 place specific responsibilities on local authorities in respect of safeguarding and promoting the welfare of children within their area who are in need and a duty to make necessary enquiries to enable the making of a decision as to whether any action should be taken to protect a child in their area.

Partnership with families and CVS

The Children Act also develops the concept of working in partnership with parents. Indeed *Principles and Practice in Regulations and Guidance* (Department of Health, 1990b) states that

> 'parents are individuals with needs of their own and even though services may be offered primarily on behalf of their children parents are entitled to help and consideration in their own right'.

It goes on to state that just as

'some young people are more vulnerable than others so are some mothers and fathers. Their parenting capacity may be limited temporarily or permanently by poverty, racism, poor housing or unemployment, by personal or marital problems, life experience, lack of parenting skills or inability to provide adequate care which should not be equated with lack of affection or with irresponsibility...

The development of working in partnership with parents is usually the most effective route to providing supplementary or substitute care for their children. Measures which antagonise, alienate, undermine or marginalise parents are counter productive.'

The Family Rights Group in 1991 defined partnership as follows:

'It is marked by respect for one another, rights to information, accountability, competence and value according to individual input. In short, each partner is seen as having something to contribute, power is shared, decisions are made jointly, roles are not only respected but also backed by a legal and moral alliance.' (Family Rights Group, 1991)

Does the use of CVS comply with these principles? A parent, usually a mother, comes into hospital with her child in cooperation with members of the medical profession and with the expectation of help. The parent is then videoed, unknown to them and without their consent, and may later be arrested by the police.

None of the principles and issues described above can be lightly dismissed. Clearly the use of CVS is directly in conflict with these principles. There are times, however, when it is impossible to work in full partnership with parents without jeopardising the safety of the child. Such conflicts also occur to a greater or lesser degree in other situations which social workers encounter.

In weighing up the principles, precedence must surely go to the child. Taking action against the parent is not the primary objective of CVS but is rather the secondary factor, arising from the diagnosis of the child's condition and the need to protect vulnerable children. Indeed in some cases, the intervention of the police and legal proceedings may not only protect the child but secure for the parent any help they may need.

An inter-agency protocol for CVS

The development of the inter-agency protocol aimed to recognise the need to protect children and to ensure that decision making is informed and reflects the contributions that differing agencies and expertise can bring.

The procedures detailed in the protocol are designed to establish clearly whether there are any grounds for concern about the child's care, in a manner that provides safeguards from further possible harm. Indeed, the primary objective of any action by agencies in following the protocol is the welfare and safety of the child. This demands good cooperation between all the professionals involved, an open-minded response to concerns and a focus on the best interests of the child throughout any agency intervention. It is essential, too, that any action taken fits within existing inter-agency procedures.

MSBP referrals by outside consultants were initially made directly to the paediatric consultants in North Staffordshire. Little or no consideration was given to involving other agencies. This was of concern to Area Child Protection Committee agencies. It meant there was no opportunity to consider either the problem or the information and help that other non-medical agencies could provide. It also meant that children could be referred to another part of the country when other help might have been more effectively offered in the area where the child and family lived. If there were concerns for the safety of the child, child protection procedures could be instigated in the area where the child lived.

The protocol states that when a referring paediatrician considers that cyanotic apnoeic episodes are possibly due to abuse by a parent or carer, a referral will be made to the local social services department and a strategy meeting will take place to consider how investigation of the concern will proceed. This meeting will be an inter-agency meeting. Membership will include other health colleagues, social services department staff and police officers. This meeting will clarify the medical history and details of concern, and will consider whether any further investigation is needed by relevant agencies, including the possible collection of additional physiological data.

If it is then decided that a referral should be made to North Staffordshire Hospital, a further meeting is held under Staffordshire Area Child Protection Committee's procedures. This meeting comprises representatives from the medical profession (nurses and hospital manager), social services department staff, police and legal representatives from both the child's local authority and Staffordshire. Representatives are also sought from the social services, police, paediatric and other health professionals from the area where the child normally resides. Within these discussions, consideration is given as to whether CVS, medical investigation or both are required. There must be a consideration of the risk to the child if the child remains at home with or without social work and health visitor involvement. If there is evidence to suggest that other action such as the commencement of care proceedings will protect the child from harm, CVS will not be used. For some children, however, the use of CVS can be the only way to identify the source and cause of the health risk to the child. Legal advice is considered essential in reaching such decisions.

If it is agreed that CVS should be used, the meeting identifies and records the lead agency or individual responsible for arranging issues such as the nursing supervision of the patient, allocation of child protection social worker and police officer, the organisation of trained staff to undertake surveillance, and arrangements for dealing with the child and planning for other children in the family in the event of detection of the abuse. This list is not exclusive.

During the discussions, attention is given to the type of video and electronic equipment that should be used to ensure that it comes up to the standards required by the police and can be used in court proceedings.

The electronic systems for alerting the ward staff to the need to intervene to prevent harm to the child are rigorous and are checked before the use of CVS.

Attention is paid to the training of the nursing staff who will undertake the surveillance and safeguards built in to minimise the fatigue of the observers. The training given to the nursing staff encompasses key papers on the subject of imposed upper airway obstruction and on the Area Child Protection Committee protocol. They are shown video recordings where abuse of a child has been demonstrated and are made familiar with the use of equipment. The hospital needs to ensure that they know how to alert staff to actual or possible abuse to the child. An assessment then takes place to determine their understanding and their response to the information given.

It is quite clear that while CVS is taking place, there is a need to prevent the child from coming to harm. If it becomes evident that harmful behaviour is taking place then the child must be protected and the harm brought to an end. Clearly the primary responsibility for this lies with the hospital. There are clear legal duties of care placed on the health authority, which needs to be able to demonstrate that it is meeting this responsibility. The safeguards built into the protocol enable this duty to be met.

The observers are also instructed that the absolute priority is protection of the child. A balance has to be struck between gaining information for use in evidence and the protection of the child. Observers are alerted to the fact that although CVS has been used when children are thought to have been subject to attempts of suffocation, it is possible that other harm may be caused to the child such as hitting or severe shaking. If this occurs, intervention of staff is necessary.

At all times the child must remain within the view of the video cameras and at no time should the parents undergo CVS independently of the child. This emphasises the aim to protect children through a focus on the parent/child interaction as opposed to general observation of the parent.

The development of the inter-agency protocol for dealing with the use of CVS has led to increased inter-agency cooperation and understanding. It has also protected the lives of some vulnerable young children. It is a regrettable fact of life that some parents abuse their children. The use of CVS provides unequivocal diagnosis of child abuse for a group of children where such proof is characteristically beset with uncertainty. It is important that all of us realise and remember that its use is limited to a small group of children. Over a period from October 1992 to October 1994, 20 children have been subject to this process. Of this 20, 16 children have been found to have suffered abuse such as attempted suffocation by hand, suffocation by pillow, fractures. Ten emergency protection orders were made and three police protection orders.

These 20 children were also referred from authorities all over the country, there were only two from Staffordshire. The numbers must be placed in context: In Staffordshire there are 550 children on the child protection register. According to the Department of Health, there are 32,500 children on child protection registers in England.

The use of CVS is not a procedure to be used for large numbers of children. For the small group of children where inter-agency discussions cannot provide alternative ways of protecting them from harm, CVS may be an appropriate method to use. The use of the inter-agency protocol is aimed at this group and has brought CVS into existing inter-agency child protection work.

References

Children's Rights Development Unit (1989) *The United Nations Convention on the Rights of the Child.* Artisan

Department of Health (1990a) *The Children Act 1989.* HMSO

Department of Health (1990b) *The Care of Children Principles and Practice in Regulations and Guidance.* HMSO

Family Rights Group (1991) *The Children Act: Partnership with Families.* HMSO

7. Covert video surveillance as a tool in child protection investigations: a social work perspective

Martin Banks, Social Worker, Staffordshire Social Services

Background

The discussion of covert video surveillance (CVS), both in the professional literature and in the popular media, has tended to focus on the medical perspective of this approach. CVS has been written about by paediatricians and practised in a hospital environment. Discussion from a social worker perspective has concentrated on some of the difficulties: issues of ethics, on which Thomas (1994) comments; and issues of possible discrimination against women, specifically mothers, which has concerned O'Hagan (1995). The business of child protection, however, is a multi-professional activity and, as Shaw points out in the previous chapter, CVS as a tool in child protection can only safely operate within clear interagency agreements which recognise the roles and responsibilities of each profession and agency to 'work together'.

From the perspective of social work, CVS is an investigating tool which can inform decisions about whether a child is suffering significant harm and also about the seriousness of any abuse: factors that are critical in assessing risk to the child and in planning protection. The central concern for social workers is phenomenological rather than ideological: what is happening to this child rather than what structures or relationships made it likely to happen. This chapter aims to describe the development and practice of CVS and then to comment on some of the issues that can be drawn from the outcomes.

The nature of CVS

There are some basic points about CVS that need to be re-emphasised. Its validity is as a method of clarifying what is happening to a child; it is a technique of last resort. Its use is limited to a minority of situations: the Staffordshire protocol on CVS (described in Chapter 6) limits its use to potentially life-threatening abuse and to investigations in which other sources of information are inconclusive. It has been used outside the United Kingdom as well as in United Kingdom settings.

The concept of Munchausen syndrome by proxy (MSBP) as a form of child abuse represents the adoption of a medical model of phenomenological description within a context where a number of disciplines are expected by social policy to 'work together': it brings together health, social work and criminal justice. What is happening to a child is described in the terms of this 'syndrome'. This represents a concern for the child's protection and leads to a set of organisational systems that underpin child protection practice.

Munchausen syndrome by proxy

The identification of the phenomenon, and the label MSBP itself, can be traced to work by Meadow, a paediatrician. In an article published in *The Lancet*, he described how children were poisoned by a parent while a false history was given about the onset of the child's illness, leading to intrusive and distressing medical interventions to determine the aetiology of the child's ill-health (Meadow, 1977). Meadow suggested that the complex nature of the abuse and in particular the way in which induced illness in the child led the carer to a close relationship with health professionals, apparently meeting the parent's needs, was in itself highly unusual and unlike the patterns seen with other forms of child abuse. Meadow refers to the role of the police and the social services department in this early article, but much of the literature that follows is dominated by a medical model of illness and the issues of differential diagnosis and treatment.

Meadow and others (Meadow, 1985; Bools and others 1991, 1993) develop through their research and describe in the literature, a broad picture of the features that can be presented to clinicians. Meadow describes six key features that should alert paediatricians (1985). He describes management and diagnosis as a clinical exercise and in his early writing was cautious in his view of inter-agency working, particularly the case conference (1985, p387). Some social work commentators have seized on this, as O'Hagan does (1995), to suggest the concept itself is primarily a construct of powerful men, to the detriment of mothers. Later writing from Meadow and others, however, acknowledges the need for working together within the framework of child protection procedures (Meadow, 1994; Bools and others, 1993; Samuels and Southall, 1992).

Bools and others (1991) stress the possibility of more than one child in a family being affected and accept the multi-disciplinary assessment needed in such cases. Follow-up research (Bools and others, 1993) highlights the worst outcomes for children who remained with the parent – always defined as the mother – who was thought to have abused the child. The work also points to the continuing psychological damage sustained by children removed from the alleged abuser. The psychological profile of the alleged abuser typically includes disrupted experience of their own child-hood, frequently including emotional abuse as well as continuing personality disorder (Bools and others, 1994). Samuels and South-all have reported case study material and diagnostic methods to identify in particular smothering by carers (Southall, Samuels and others, 1987; Samuels and Southall, 1992; Samuels and others, 1992). They argue the need for clear 'diagnosis' (Samuels and Southall, 1992, p759) in order to enable the child to be protected. Their case study material is used to provide a clear typology of the phenomena: in terms of the abuse itself; characteristics of the abusing parent – usually the mother – in terms of mental health; and observations on management.

The paediatric research in this area follows a common theme. Clinicians are presented with a child who is demonstrably ill, in many cases seriously so. A wide range of tests and investigations fails to identify causation; the illness does not fit any coherent pattern. The suspicion therefore develops that the child is being deliberately harmed. The case study material documents unequiv-ocally some of the ways in which adults harm children: poisoning, suffocation, administration of inappropriate drugs and tampering with life-supporting apparatus (Samuels and Southall, 1992). These actions are profoundly different in their seriousness for the child compared with some of the other behaviours that have been given the same label of 'Munchausen syndrome by proxy', such as falsifying the child's temperature record or adding parental blood to a nappy to give the impression of serious illness in the child. Factitious illness may lead to inappropriate and distressing med-ical procedures for the child, and may indicate a relationship with adult carers that might be described as emotionally abusive. The potential seriousness for the child of imposed illness, however, includes long-term physiological damage and, at worst, death.

One of the difficulties in the literature on MSBP is that a focus on the adult carer and the carer's emotional needs may obscure the needs of the child. Harm of such a level of severity is relatively uncommon in social work practice. Its discussion can appear melodramatic. However, where the potential seriousness of harm is of this level, those involved in child protection need to focus very clearly on the child's needs first and foremost.

The use of CVS

CVS was developed nearly ten years ago as a method of establishing beyond doubt whether a child suffering recurrent episodes of apnoea was in fact being smothered. Extensive examination, including investigation of the throat under general anaesthetic, provided no indication of any organic cause for these episodes. Yet the child was seen to have episodes of unconsciousness from which resuscitation was needed. Each episode seemed to have commenced in the presence of the same carer (Southall and others, 1987). After multi-agency discussion, police officers undertook observation using closed circuit television and video recording of events, and the carer was seen to place a T-shirt over the child's face and mouth while he struggled. Physiological recordings of the child indicated to the paediatrician that air flow to the child was restricted. Intervention took place and legal action ensued both in the civil – or care – court and the criminal court.

This early case study has been described in some detail because it includes many of the features that characterise a number of situations where agencies have chosen to use covert observation through closed circuit television or 'covert video surveillance'. Common strands have been documented in a number of children who were found to have been abused in similar ways and where this approach was used as a tool in assessment of the abuse (Samuels and others, 1992). The children were observed to suffer attempts at suffocation with the parent's hands, with fabric or with clingfilm. Covert surveillance followed concerns that the child had suffered apparently life-threatening episodes of apnoea which could not be readily explained in terms of physiology and which always commenced in the care of the same adult. A similar set of circumstances is documented in the law reports of a care case heard by the High Court (reported as Re: D.H. (A Minor) (Child Abuse) at [1994] 1 FLR.) The experience of children referred to paediatricians in Staffordshire has been on very similar lines.

The children have typically been very young, between a few weeks and two years old. All have had extensive medical investigation for apparent life-threatening illness, predominantly apnoea and cyanotic episodes. All the children have been seen to be ill, by ambulance personnel or casualty staff. All suffered the onset of episodes of illness in the care of one parent only. Parents in each case were unable to consider any explanation of their child's situation other than the one they themselves proposed: that the child was critically ill. Of those children whose parents remained with them on the hospital ward after a decision to use CVS, 18 out of a total of 20 were then seen to be abused. The nature of abuse has included attempts at suffocation, with the hand or a pillow, poisoning attempts (administration of sterilising fluid through a naso-gastric line), the insertion of a toothbrush down a toddler's throat and, prior to the implementation of a protocol on safe practice, deliberate breaking of a baby's arm. None of the situations was felt by nurses, doctors, police officers or social workers to be anything other than harmful to the child. Where ambiguous events occurred, video recording was monitored by professionals before the child was again left alone with the carer.

Observation of the interaction between parent and child also provides other indicators of a dysfunctional relationship, however: verbal abuse of the child, smacking, prodding and shaking the child, and demands by the adult for affection and for demonstrations of love from very young children. Such episodes can be interrupted in the interests of child and of parent. Even brief observation, however, throws light on very stressed relationships between a parent and a young child and provides the context in which more serious abuse may occur. The follow-up research by Bools and others (1994) found the same factors in some parents: a perception by them of the child as rejecting at the time of the suffocation. There are parallels with the experiences of parents who fatally abuse their children, who have described the child as rejecting or as developmentally abnormal (Korbin, 1987).

The whole of the interaction needs to be assessed by those who have to make decisions on the child's protection, in order to form an assessment of the relationship. It is important to note that the kinds of adult behaviour which may occur can be highly bizarre, not in themselves a reaction to the stresses of life with a sick child with which paediatric nurses are very familiar.

Social work and CVS

In terms of social work practice, it is the seriousness of the events of abuse that are significant and that make it necessary to consider investigative approaches such as CVS. Assigning a label to a parent or carer of a child is less helpful than a detailed analysis of two questions: is the child being abused, and if so, can she or he be protected with the information available?

The difficulties for social work of CVS have been defined in terms of parents' rights and have given rise to observations on equal opportunities: in particular O'Hagan's suggestion that as mothers are often identified as the abuser, the technique is intrinsically sexist (O'Hagan and Dillinger, 1995). The literature reveals little or nothing on issues of ethnicity or class.

Analysis of CVS needs to consider seriously issues of oppression. However, O'Hagan's concerns overlook the central issue of power in this context: that of adult over child. The argument used to justify the use CVS of is, as he suggests, the need to protect the interests of the child. This is the case throughout child protection practice, however, and underpins the ideology of social work in child protection (see, for example, Fox Harding, 1991). The very young child with whom CVS is concerned, is in most respects utterly disempowered in relation to adults. In these cases, the adult further reinforces domination and oppression by suffocating or poisoning the child. It is on this power dynamic that social work initially needs to focus. In any work with abusers, the context that led to abuse needs to be clearly identified. Social work needs also to consider the rights of parents and, as Thomas has observed (1994), the practice of CVS can subjugate partnership with parents to the process of clarifying whether the child is being abused. The primary purpose, however, is not to gain criminal evidence but to establish if serious abuse is present, where no other means can detect it. If it is, then professionals can protect the child and also begin to be honest about the level of risk involved, which is a prerequisite of partnership.

Relatively little has been written on MSBP from a social work perspective. It is notably lacking in readily accessed social policy material: *Working Together* notes MSBP as a reason for registration on local authorities' child protection registers (para 6.40). Joint working has developed, under some direction from central government, to reflect the uneasy balance in social policy between non-intervention in families and the protection of children from abuse (Fox Harding, 1991; Parton, 1991). Moreover, particularly since the Cleveland report (1988), the importance of testing of professional opinion in court is emphasised. In the Cleveland case, the power was shifted from the paediatric opinion – that sexual abuse had taken place – to the judiciary. To achieve protection of children, the professionals involved have to work together to the standards demanded by central government and enforced by the legal system.

Non-accidental poisoning or smothering represent a particularly extreme form of child abuse. They are relatively uncommon. Yet the risks of permanent physical or psychological damage are considerable (Bools and others, 1991, 1993; Porter and others, 1994). This sort of behaviour is difficult to accept and believe, even for judges (Samuels and Southall, 1992). Such abuse presents challenges to the way in which social workers and social policy view the balance of children's rights and those of parents.

The Department of Health has recently suggested that MSBP represents an area where partnership may need to be curtailed because of what is called the 'deviousness' of perpetrators (Department of Health, 1994). The language is pejorative but social work practice has long recognised that partnership is a two-way process and that a reduction in danger to children is unlikely if risks to children are not acknowledged. By unravelling myth and pretence in adult-child interaction, it may be that clarity of assessment brought by CVS can assist any meaningful partnership. The literature on MSBP has marked a gradual move away from hopes that confrontation by professionals of the carer might bring acknowledgement of responsibility. Parents can find the suggestion of ill-treatment of their child impossible to accept (Mehl and others, 1990; Bools and others, 1994), as in other forms of child abuse. In social work we have long recognised that failure to identify or quantify risk, for whatever good intention, can be dangerous to the children we want to help (Dale and others, 1984). Such danger is characterised by a lack of objectivity, both by adult carers and by professionals: it is objectivity that observation of these children can offer.

Child protection work has struggled with the balance of responsibilities between parents' rights and intervention aimed at protection of children from harm. Social work has often been seen to be in a pivotal position in this balance and in decisions about protection for which social workers are ultimately accountable. Lewis (1994), commenting on decision making in child protection, summarises some of the problems previous writers identified in making decisions in child protection, including over-optimism, cultural relativism, a lack of explicit criteria and a shortage of factual information. In dealing with highly vulnerable children, possibly subject to life-threatening abuse, decision making needs to be based on information that is as clear as possible about what is happening in the child's life: is the child really being abused or not?

It is only with clarity about the phenomenon that rational decisions can be reached. For a few very young children who are faced
with potentially life-threatening abuse, where all the other information is inconclusive, CVS provides a vehicle to protect them and
begin a process of positive change.

References

Bools, C N, Neale, B A, Meadow, S R (1992) 'Co-morbidity associated with fabricated illness (Munchausen syndrome by proxy)',
Archives of Disease in Childhood, 67, 77–79

Bools, C N, Neale, B A, Meadow, S R (1993) 'Follow-up of victims
of fabricated illness (Munchausen syndrome by proxy)',
Archives of Disease in Childhood, 69, 6, 625–630

Bools, C N, Neale, B A, Meadow, S R (1994) 'Munchausen syndrome by proxy: a study of psychopathology', *Child Abuse and
Neglect*, 18 (9)

Dale, P, Davies, M, Morrison, T, Waters, J (1984) *Dangerous Families: assessment and treatment in child abuse*, Tavistock

Department of Health (1991) *Working Together Under the Children Act 1989: a guide to arrangements for inter-agency cooperation for the protection of children from abuse*. HMSO

Department of Health (1994) *The Challenge of Partnership*.
HMSO

Fox Harding, L (1991) *Perspectives in Child Care Policy*. Longman

Korbin, J E (1987) 'Incarcerated mothers' perceptions and interpretations of their fatally maltreated children', *Child Abuse and
Neglect*, 11 (3), 397–407

Lewis, A (1994) *Chairing Child Protection Conferences*. Avebury

Meadow, S R (1977) 'Munchausen syndrome by proxy: the hinterland of child abuse', *The Lancet*, ii, 343–345

Meadow, S R (1985) 'Management of Munchausen syndrome by
proxy', *Archives of Disease in Childhood*, 60, 383–393

Meadow, S R (1994) 'Munchausen syndrome by proxy', *Journal of
Clinical Forensic Medicine*, 1, 121–127

Mehl, A L, Coble, L, Johnson, S (1990) 'Munchausen syndrome by
proxy: a family affair', *Child Abuse and Neglect*, 14, 577

O'Hagan, K (29.10.95) Letter, *Community Care*

O'Hagan, K and Dillinger, K (1995) *The abuse of women within
childcare work*. Open University Press

Parton, N (1991) *Governing the Family*, Macmillan

Porter, G E, Heitsch, G M, Millar M D (1994) 'Munchausen syndrome by proxy: unusual manifestations and disturbing
sequelae', *Child Abuse and Neglect*, 18 (9)

Samuels, M P and Southall, D P (1992) 'Munchausen syndrome by proxy', *British Journal of Hospital Medicine*, 47 (10), 759–762

Samuels, M P, McLaughlin, W, Jacobsen, R R, Poets, C F, Southall, D P (1992) 'Fourteen cases of imposed upper airway obstruction', *Archives of Disease in Childhood*, 67, 162–170

Southall, D, Samuels, M P and others (1987) 'Apnoeic episodes induced by smothering: two cases identified by covert video surveillance', *British Medical Journal*, 294, 1637–1641

Thomas, T (1994) 'Covert Video Surveillance in Child Protection Work', *Family Law*, September, 524–526

8. Munchausen syndrome by proxy: a police perspective

Detective Inspector John Fox, Hampshire Police Authority

The role of the police in cases of Munchausen syndrome by proxy (MSBP) is sometimes unclear and inconsistent. Opinions vary between professionals about whether the police, and therefore ultimately the criminal courts, should be used to investigate what is seen by many people to be a medical problem.

MSBP is a form of child abuse, and therefore the perpetrator may well have committed a serious crime. It is not an illness like measles, it is a general term used to describe behaviour by the carer of a child which in law often constitutes assault, poisoning, neglect and even homicide. The classic 'smothering' situation which most people associate with MSBP, although common, is by no means the only form of abuse. There are many other far more dangerous and subtle forms of inducing or fabricating illness, many of which leave the victim with irreparable damage, as is demonstrated in the case studies that follow.

In this chapter, I will use three case studies: a child poisoned with ant powder and later injected with a potassium chloride solution; a child starved to death while at home and in hospital and a sibling nearly killed in the same way; and a child who at three years old had undergone many surgical explorations and operations to cure a 'feeding problem' that did not exist. The case studies are intended to demonstrate how an earlier referral and investigation utilising child protection procedures would have spared the respective children a great deal of suffering. It will be shown how classic signs that MSBP was being perpetrated were either not seen or were ignored by medical staff, social workers and police officers and that professionals failed to work together in protecting the children involved.

Case 1: Paul

An 11-month-old baby, Paul, was taken to a general practitioner by his mother, Jenny. The general practitioner was told that the child had been sick and he was shown a tin of baby milk powder which appeared to have some light grey powder mixed into it. The child appeared perfectly well and was sent home with a suggestion that the milk be returned to the chemist from whence it came.

That evening, Jenny phone the general practitioner and said that Paul, '....had vomited again, was unsettled and screaming, and had an episode during which his colour became blue and his expression vacant.' (Jenny is an ex-paediatric nurse.) The general practitioner again saw Paul and although he could find nothing wrong with him, arranged an urgent admission to hospital. Jenny and Paul left in their own transport to go to the casualty department. They arrived an hour and a half later; the journey normally takes five minutes. On admission Paul was gravely ill. He was convulsing and fitting so seriously that he could easily have died. The fitting was controlled after ten or fifteen minutes, using diazepam, and Paul was taken to the intensive care unit.

The police were called in to investigate the apparent contamination of the baby milk by a person unknown. (Forensic tests later revealed that the grey powder in the tin of baby milk was ant powder which contained chlordane, a small amount of which could be fatal to small children if ingested.) The implications of such an investigation for the manufacturer are enormous and all such tins were seized from the chemist concerned.

There were one or two inconsistencies in Jenny's story when she was spoken to by a police officer, but these were put down to the stress of having a seriously ill child. Jenny spent the night with Paul in a cubicle on the intensive care unit and over the next few hours several unexplained events occurred, including the drip feed being turned off twice on separate occasions; Paul's breathing becoming erratic; and he suffered a cardiac arrest. All these things happened when only Jenny was with Paul in the cubicle.

Early in the morning, Jenny was found (by nurses) with a stolen box of potassium chloride ampoules. When the box was recovered, one ampoule was missing. Also missing from her cubicle were two hypodermic syringes. The police were not informed of any of these events and carried on their investigation into the contamination of the milk powder. Jenny was allowed to stay alone with Paul for two more nights and in the meantime the police shared the inconsistencies in her story with a paediatrician. He also had concerns but declined to say what they were at that time.

The following day, however, the paediatrician told police of the events described above. Jenny was arrested and subsequently admitted feeding Paul the ant powder to get him admitted to hospital. She said that during the night she had turned off the drip feed and injected Paul with a solution containing the potassium chloride (a potentially fatal drug). When her house was searched, not only was the ant powder found, but next to her bed a book describing how a nurse in a children's hospital in Texas fatally injected several of her patients in order to seek attention.

Jenny's history showed that she had presented many times to her own and other general practitioners with factitious ailments; and that another older child had been taken to hospital several times with reports of vomiting, blood in urine, and two 'blue floppy fits' when breathing apparently stopped. She seemed a sad, lonely woman who did not get on well with her husband, who was a busy professional man. She had previously come to the attention of the police for making hoax emergency calls and obtaining controlled painkillers by deception, but this did not become apparent for several days because the police did not think to check her in their records.

If an open mind had been kept by everyone and basic background checks been done on Jenny and her older child, a worrying picture may have emerged and Paul may have been spared several life-threatening incidents. The children, who appear to have suffered no long-term physical harm, were made the subject of care proceedings, and at crown court Jenny received a probation order.

Case 2: James and Mary
A boy, James, was born to a young mother, Helen who, almost from his birth, reported that he was vomiting after every feed. He was re-admitted to hospital for tests but no apparent cause was found and no unusual vomiting was observed by medical staff. There then followed a year during which James put on virtually no weight, was in and out of hospital and was being fed by increasingly desperate means including intravenous total parental nutrition (T.P.N). After 11 months, James died. His weight then was virtually the same as his birth weight (Figure 3).

Despite many medical tests and procedures, including a fundoplication (a tightening of the muscles at the top of the stomach to prevent vomiting), no cause was found for his apparent inability to digest food and thrive. In the end, his pain was so great that increasing doses of pain-killers had to be administered and the proximate cause of death was in fact morphine poisoning. There was no post-mortem and the case was never reported to the coroner. When James still had five months to live, the paediatrician treating him suggested to the social services department at the hospital that he thought the mother might be withholding feeds and that there was a strong suspicion of Munchausen syndrome by proxy (MSBP). No referral was ever made to the police and no further investigation was carried out into this suggestion.

Figure 3 James

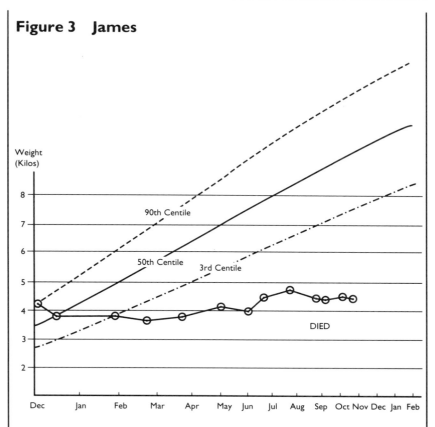

A year later, another child, Mary, was born to the family. Again, almost from birth, this child was reported by her mother to be vomiting after every feed and was admitted to hospital. As before, nothing was found to be wrong and no excessive vomiting was seen by staff. Over the next few months, Mary fell into a pattern similar to that of James, putting on no weight despite being put on the full range of feeding methods including T.P.N. During that time she was in and out of hospital but no medical reason could be found for her failure to thrive. Luckily, the same paediatrician who cared for and tried to save James was now dealing with Mary. When she was four months old, he again told the social services department that they must consider MSBP. Again, no referral was made to the police and no child protection investigation was started.

When Mary was five months old, as a final attempt to find the cause of her problems, she was sent to a major children's hospital and an eminent paediatric gastro-enterologist began to tackle the case. When she arrived at that hospital, he described her as being in an extremely dangerous position because of gross malnutrition. Indeed, if the intravenous feeding had been stopped for any length of time, he believed that she would have died within a short time. What he quickly established, however, was that there was nothing medically wrong with the girl. He realised, perhaps because of his greater experience, that Mary's mother was preventing a proper feeding programme by tampering with feeding lines, tipping away milk, and generally discouraging Mary from feeding. Without doing anything other than the original hospital had done except ensure that the mother could no longer interfere with the prescribed feeds, this paediatrician was able to double Mary's weight within two months. By the time she was discharged back to the original hospital, although still below the third centile, she was no longer in danger and was feeding normally from a bottle as well as having solids (Figure 4).

Figure 4   Mary

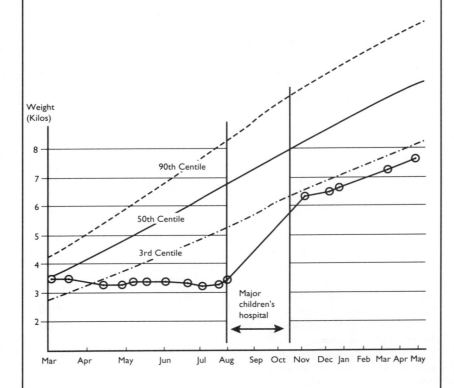

A child protection conference made the decision to discharge Mary from hospital and allowed her home in the care of her mother. She was placed on the local child protection register, but no legal order was sought to protect her. Although a police officer attended the conference as is usual and heard the paediatrician say that he considered all Mary's problems to be the result of MSBP, no investigation was commenced. It was not until several months and three conferences later that links were made between James's and Mary's medical histories. Only then did the police take notice and start to look back at the history of these children.

The investigation took months. A team of officers interviewed numerous nurses and doctors who had been involved with the family; they uncovered a history of abuse and a lack of knowledge among some key professionals as to what MSBP actually was. This lack of knowledge is best illustrated by a note found on Mary's social services file which said, among other things '...It is suspected that this child may have Munchausens Disease.' Clearly whoever wrote that thought MSBP was something like measles. It was also undoubtedly because of lack of knowledge among the police that no investigation was started after the first case conference.

The police went through all the medical notes and produced a 'sequence of events chart'. It emerged that the number of problems with the feeding equipment for both children was not only uncannily similar but far greater than could ever be expected normally, (Figure 5). Indeed when the events were properly listed, the paediatric gastro-enterologist who treated Mary said, 'Whilst tubes and lines, on occasions, fall out I have never met patients in which tubes or lines have become damaged or have been removed, or have fallen out as frequently as in these two children.' In James's life, there were 17 occasions when a problem occurred with his feeding equipment. Had the original suspicions of the paediatrician been referred on to the police, perhaps they would have been able to gather evidence to ascertain whether the tubes were being tampered with.

One of the other things that the investigation revealed was that Helen (in the words of one senior ward sister) '...was to turn out to be the most difficult mother of a sick child (she) was ever dealt with in (her) nursing experience'. First, she insisted on doing nearly all the care of both children herself, which included administering their feeding. She insisted on always being in a 'cubicle' rather than the open ward and always kept the curtains shut, making it difficult for staff to monitor the child. She also frequently upset people by repeatedly 'flying off the handle'.

There is no doubt that a lot of staff were intimidated by Helen, yet with others she formed a close relationship, the effect being that at ward meetings the staff were completely divided about her and professional, objective judgements were clouded. When she eventually left

Figure 5   Problems with feeding equipment

James	Mary
Naso-gastric tube pulled out.	Feeding tube pulled out.
Nasto-gastric tube pulled out.	Hole found in feeding tube.
Naso-gastric tube not working properly.	Central intravenous feeding line split at hub, believed to be due to twisting of hub.
Naso-gastric tube loose.	
Naso-gastric tube filter leaking.	Central line broken – further repair attempted.
Central line separated.	Central line disconnected.
Naso-gastric tube removed.	Naso-gastric tube became displaced.
Central line blocked.	Central intravenous feeding line blocked.
Naso-gastric tube coughed up.	Central line displaced.
Central venous feeding line disconnected.	Mother observed pulling on central line.
Central line blocked.	Naso-gastric tube removed.
Tube half pulled out.	Naso-gastric tube pulled out.
Tube pulled out.	
Line blocked.	
Tube fell out.	
Tube blocked.	

the paediatric hospital with Mary, many nurses had to receive counselling and psychiatric help to cope with the distress she had caused
them. An example of this is that when she was moved out of her cubicle
onto the open ward so that a nurse could monitor the feeds 24-hours a
day, Helen objected violently and literally fought with the nurses trying to move her belongings.

During the police investigation, Mary was at home with her mother
and her weight was just creeping up, never reaching the third centile.
She had some reported urinary tract infections and then a sudden bout
of anaemia, the most likely cause of which was deemed to be blood-let-
ting. Shortly after this, Helen was arrested by the police and the mass
of evidence gathered was put to her. There were witnesses who had
seen her deliberately mixing up a weaker solution of baby milk than
was prescribed, some who had seen her tampering with tubes, and
others who saw her ill-treat the children in other ways. All this was
documented in the notes but no one until then had collated the infor-

Addendum

Please note that the following text should be included in Chapter 8, *Munchausen syndrome by proxy: a police perspective*, at the bottom of page 104 and the top of page 105:

All this was documented in the notes but no one until then had collated the information.

Unsurprisingly, Helen instantly denied any wrongdoing but eventually she admitted twisting and breaking a tough polyurethane feeding line. (Later, at the care proceedings, she told the judge that this was 'absent minded fiddling'.) She also admitted to leaving the 24-hour feeding pump turned off for some time each day. Most of the other incidents were denied, however. It had already been decided by counsel that because of the lack of a post-mortem and other factors, there would be no point in trying to bring any charges in relation to James. Helen was therefore charged with wilfully ill-treating Mary. The evidence gathered was then turned over to solicitors acting for the social services department and care proceedings were commenced.

After full care proceedings in the high court, the judge ruled, '....I regret to say, looking at the whole of the evidence, that I am satisfied on the balance of probabilities to the high standard required, that both children were victims of Munchausen's syndrome by proxy, and that the mother was the perpetrator.' A care order was granted and Mary was placed with foster parents where, for the first time in her life, she began to thrive. Her weight quickly increased and was soon around the 50th centile. Those who knew her well noticed a tremendous change in Mary and since the care proceedings she has been much happier and more sociable. It is significant that the large weight gains and changes in her personality only occurred after her actual removal from her mother. Despite the fact that Helen had been confronted about MSBP months earlier, Mary still failed to thrive while in her care, her weight remaining around the third centile.

Although the indicators of MSBP were present, professionals did not collate the evidence necessary to make an appropriate assessment. Just before Mary was sent to the other hospital, at that time close to death, a social services manager wrote to a colleague saying, 'Currently we are not treating this as a child protection issue'.

Addendum

Please note that the following text should be included in Chapter 8. Munchausen syndrome by proxy at the bottom of page 104 and the top of page 105.

rently we are not treating this as a child protection issue'. This was despite the earlier death of her brother, a total of 19 unexplained 'problems' with the feeding tubes of both children, three reports from paediatricians that MSBP was suspected, two reported statements by the father of the children that he thought his wife was starving them, not to mention a wealth of other evidence in the medical notes. After a three-week trial at crown court, Helen was convicted of wilfully ill-treating Mary. She was given a probation order for three years with instructions from the judge that she does not care for any children during that time.

Case 3: Luke

A boy, Luke, was born to a single young mother, Sandra. There were some complications at birth and Luke needed a prolonged spell in hospital and an operation. His mother stayed with him in hospital and reported to staff that he was unable to keep his feed down. She reported that Luke vomited several times a day and either she or a nurse duly wrote this fact on his 'infant feed chart'.

For the next three years, Luke spent many months in different hospitals while doctors tried to find a cause for his lack of ability to feed. Many operations were performed on him, including a fundoplication (see Case 2) and a laparotomy, both major types of surgery. In addition, over the years, Luke was fitted with an assortment of feeding devices progressing from a naso-gastric tube to a jejenostomy tube which passes feed straight through the abdominal wall into the intestine beyond the stomach and required surgery. The escalation of the various feeding methods was considered necessary because of the continued assertions of the mother that Luke could not accept or digest anything.

As with Case 2, no medical evidence was ever found to suggest why he could not feed properly. He was given intravenous feeding or tube feeding so many times that by the age of three he had hundreds of scars where incisions had been made on his body. Indeed, there were at least 30 old entry sites on one side of his neck alone. In addition to the reported vomiting, on several occasions problems occurred whereby Luke's feeding tubes 'fell out' or 'broke'. Each time this happened he had to undergo another operation to re-insert it.

By chance, Luke and his mother moved to the catchment area of the hospital where the children in Case 2 were treated. He was also treated by the same paediatrician who was now even more aware of MSBP and its effect. This paediatrician began to suspect that there was nothing medically wrong with Luke and after a month-long admission, during which his feeding tubes became faulty three times, the paediatrician called an inter-agency meeting to discuss the case. The police were present and immediately agreed to investigate. A system was set up whereby the police would know if Sandra tampered with Luke's feeding tube. Only a handful of people were aware that the police were working in the hospital and there was no disruption whatsoever to ward life.

The day after the investigation began, Luke's jejenostomy tube (about 18 inches of which was in his body) was found to be completely removed. Sandra took it to a nurse, saying that it had spontaneously been coughed up. Police enquiries revealed that in fact she had deliberately pulled it out of his body. Sandra was then quietly taken to a side room by staff, where she was arrested by a detective. She initially denied any wrongdoing but shortly afterwards asked to be interviewed, whereupon she made a full confession to cutting or pulling out tubes on many occasions and falsely reporting for years that Luke has been vomiting after every attempt to feed him conventionally.

Luke's three years of pain and misery was therefore over within two days of an inter-agency referral being made. He was given conventional food for the first time in his life and it was found that he could eat and digest it perfectly normally. Within two weeks he was out of hospital and was soon eating a normal diet. What he will have with him for the rest of his life, however, are the dreadful scars from the hundreds of operations performed on him. In later life, he may have problems with his stomach due to the scar tissue inside and of course he may never recover emotionally from the virtual loss of the first three years of his childhood.

Sandra said that she had wanted to keep him ill and in hospital because she craved the attention she was given by friends, family and staff because she had a 'sick' child. She was relieved that she had been caught and that her behaviour, which she was unable to control, would stop. A care order was granted in respect of Luke and he is now living happily with relatives. He goes to playschool and is starting to make a relatively normal childhood. Sandra pleaded guilty at crown court to wilful cruelty and was given a long probation order. She is receiving psychiatric help and sees Luke regularly.

Practice dilemmas in suspected cases of MSBP

My experience has shown clearly that many in the medical profession do not find it easy first to believe that the carer of a child patient could be harming that patient and second, to report any suspicions they may have to the child protection agencies. This is quite understandable, as doctors and nurses are encouraged to work in partnership with parents of sick children and their working relationship has to be one of trust and compassion. A close bond is often formed between parent and healer as they strive to find the cause of the mystery illness affecting the child.

It is well reported (Rosenberg, 1987) that perpetrators of MSBP sometimes show great sympathy and understanding for the worry and frustration of the paediatrician struggling to find a cure. A good example of this is found in Case 2, where Helen appeared to become over familiar with the consultant paediatrician, always using his christian name and genuinely appearing to share his frustration and worry. Another senior member of the medical staff became a close friend of the family and would attend child protection conferences as Helen's supporter. In cases where these relationships breach professional boundaries, confusion is added to an already difficult picture.

It has also been recognised (Meadow, 1984) that perpetrators often have, or pretend to have, previous medical experience which may lull professionals into a false sense of security. Helen told people at various times that she was a qualified nurse (which was untrue), and in Case 1, Jenny was an ex-paediatric nurse, a fact that gave her story greater credibility in the eyes of her general practitioner.

Referrals are therefore frequently made only when medical staff have ruled out every alternative cause for the child's illness. In some cases, the social services department may have suspicions reported to them but may not feel it serious enough to refer it to the police, as is evident in Case 2. From the police point of view (and quite possibly the child's) that is often too late. Suspicions must be shared as soon as they are formed. In turn though, the child protection agencies must not over-react but should perhaps arrange a case discussion while monitoring developments. In Case 2, when James was being treated, it can be seen that if the police had been involved when the first suspicions were reported, they would have merely had to do a thorough check on the medical history and prepare a sequence of events chart, to say with reasonable certainty that something was amiss. Sadly, no referral was made and the child died.

Another complicating factor is that sometimes there is a perceived ethical problem in that it could be considered a breach of trust to report suspicions or to allow a discreet investigation to take place. Yet if a doctor suspected that a visitor to one of his or her patients was stealing morphine from the dangerous drugs cabinet, or stealing money from the other patients, he or she would probably have no hesitation in calling in the police and would not be too concerned about how they gathered the evidence to detect that crime. Why is it then that when a visitor to a patient is suspected of seriously assaulting that patient, there is suddenly a difficult ethical problem for the doctor to overcome before referring it and allowing the police the freedom to gather the evidence as they see fit? If we are to remain child-focused there are, in my opinion, two principles that should be uppermost in the minds of all those involved in the care of sick children:

- The child is the patient, and his or her welfare is paramount.
- Every child has the right to grow up unmolested and unabused.

Although statements like these are becoming clichéd, it is important that they are not swept into the background by the frequent calls to honour the rights and privacy of parents and always to work in partnership with them. There is no doubt that the rights of parents are important but if, for example, a discreet, low-key investigation is carried out and it is found that the parents are not abusing the child, less harm is done to them than the devastating effect on the child if he or she is being abused and no investigation is carried out. There is no perfect solution and sadly sometimes parents will be upset. If we are to keep the focus on protecting children, however, there will inevitably be cases where innocent people are caught up in the assessment process, as happens in all aspects of child protection work and, indeed, investigation into all types of crime.

The role of the police in suspected cases of MSBP

In cases of MSBP, as with other forms of abuse, it is essential that *Working Together Under the Children Act* is implemented. In addition to being a medical problem, MSBP is also a serious crime, and the prime agency in the UK for the investigation of crime is the police force. The police have worked closely with social services departments in the investigation of child abuse for several years. The bulk of the evidence gathering is carried out by the police, however, who are then responsible for presenting that evidence to a criminal court and handing it to solicitors acting for local authorities to use in care proceedings. The police have the expertise and equipment to do this and child abuse caused by MSBP should not be investigated differently from any other form of abuse. The aim is to prevent further unnecessary harm to the child, to preserve evidence, and to ensure that the perpetrator does not become aware of an impending investigation, thereby covering their tracks and perhaps continuing the abuse in some more subtle, less detectable form.

It is vital that the police understand and are sympathetic to the considerations and concerns of the other agencies. They must instil confidence in the professionals with whom they will be working and must tailor their investigation to meet what is generally felt to be the best interests of the child. The medical profession must be reassured that referring a suspicion to the police will not result in an uncontrollable monster being unleashed. Equally, the police have a job to do. They must be allowed to gather their evidence in a professional way which, if necessary, will satisfy the high standards expected by the courts. (The burden of proof in a criminal court is that of showing beyond reasonable doubt that the perpetrator committed the crime. In other words, a jury must be sure of someone's guilt to convict. Even in care proceedings, since the case Re: M, a minor, 1994, it is now the situation that the more serious the allegation, the more convincing the evidence needs to be to tip the balance in respect of it.) Case 2 illustrates how important it is for good evidence to be obtained. Confronting the mother did not stop Mary's suffering and had the care proceedings failed because of lack of evidence, her weight may well have remained hovering around the third centile and her quality of life severely impaired.

The police have to deal with an alleged perpetrator in a way prescribed by the Police and Criminal Evidence Act 1984, part of which dictates that any interview must be carried out on tape at a police station. Confrontation by a paediatrician may jeopardise any future interview that the police have with that person. It is also unfair to the suspect because they would not have been given the statutory rights and safeguards that the police are bound to give, such as the presence of a solicitor. For their part, the police must ensure that any arrest in a hospital or surgery is done in as quiet and considerate a way as possible. Plain-clothes officers should be used and the alleged perpetrator should if possible be taken quietly to a side room, away from the other patients.

Unfortunately, there is no 'nice' way to arrest someone, but a lot can be done to lessen the effect on those around at the time. One of the most important aspects from the police point of view, is that confidentiality is maintained from the outset. Knowledge of an investigation must be confined to as small a group as possible and there should be no discussion about it among colleagues who do not 'need to know'. This policy will be quite alien to many professionals, although second nature to the police. Yet it is one that is increasingly being used in other areas of child protection; for example, in cases of suspected paedophile rings. The need for MSBP perpetrators to continue their behaviour is often compulsive. If they became aware of the suspicions, perhaps by accidental loose talk in a hospital corridor, they are very likely not to stop the abuse but to continue in a more subtle, less detectable way. If it is decided to use any covert technical equipment during the investigation, it is again vitally important that this equipment is not known about, or discussed, by anyone who does not absolutely have to. This may unfortunately have to include ward staff and may pose a dilemma for a senior ward sister or nursing manager.

As with all other types of child abuse, an early strategy meeting between the small group of professionals to be involved in the investigation is extremely important. The prime agencies who must attend are health, social services and police. It is vital that from this point the number of people with knowledge of the suspicions is kept to a minimum and that a clear understanding about confidentiality is established. All discussion and decisions taken should be recorded in writing and agreed: covert video surveillance (CVS) has become the most controversial aspect of investigations into MSBP.

There are many different views about the ethics of CVS, the lack of privacy it creates, and the excellent conclusive evidence that can be obtained by its use. The police use covert equipment in the investigation of many crimes and over the years countless serious offences of all types have been successfully detected using technical equipment which is not known about by the offender. A high level of authority always has to be obtained before such equipment is used, and in each individual case its use has to be fully justified. The use of covert technical equipment will only be sanctioned if it can be demonstrated that other more conventional methods of investigation have failed or are not practical because of the circumstances. When investigating cases of MSBP, the police therefore have a valuable tool at their disposal, but one that will only be used after a great deal of thought, discussion and consideration. Any use of CVS is part of the 'evidence gathering process' and in most places would be managed by the police. This is entirely proper, not only so that first class equipment is employed that will produce evidence to the high standards required by the courts, but also because it will help to relieve medical staff of suggestions later on of acting in an underhand manner, thereby improving their chances of maintaining a good relationship with the alleged abuser while still offering the child full protection.

Working together on suspected cases of MSBP – the way forward

In areas where there is a hospital with a paediatric unit and where cases of MSBP are therefore likely to be reported, it may promote good practice if all the relevant agencies have already drawn up a 'protocol' to give guidance in the investigation, as has been pioneered by Staffordshire Area Child Protection Committee. Each case is of course different and the 'protocol' would have to give fairly loose guidelines. There are, however, some points common to any case of MSBP that could be considered in advance of a referral, thereby smoothing the way in the initial stages. A meeting to draw up such a protocol will also provide an opportunity for the professionals who will be dealing with investigations, should they arise, to get together. This would enable them to exchange ideas and get to know each other, hopefully building up some trust at the same time.

It is this trust between professionals that is so vital if we are to protect children. Many paediatricians find it difficult to call in the investigative agencies. As has already been discussed, the police must do everything they can to reassure doctors that they will carry out a delicate and sensitive investigation, particularly if it involves working on hospital premises. It is to be hoped that a meeting such as that described above will go a long way to fostering trust and removing some of the mystery about what the police will subsequently do. There are 43 police forces in England and Wales, each with their own policies: within those forces are many senior detectives, each with their own areas, who have to decide how they are going to react if a report of suspected MSBP is made to them. It will be impossible to achieve complete consistency throughout the country, and the police may well respond to referrals with varying ideas and will sometimes be unsure if and when to become involved. A meeting to discuss MSBP and to draw up a protocol suitable for the local area is a valuable investment. Below are some ideas that the police may wish to have included in such a protocol.

The management of suspected cases of MSBP

Statement of principles

The child is the patient and his or her welfare is paramount.

Every child has the right to grow up unmolested and unabused.

1.   Investigating cases of MSBP is a multiagency burden and sus-

picions or information must be shared at the earliest opportunity. Delay may cause loss of evidence or prolong the child's suffering in proven cases, whereas an early, low-key investigation could rule out MSBP and all effort can be put into finding a medical cause for the problem.

2. In accordance with the Department of Health/Home Office document *Working Together*, an early multi-agency strategy meeting should be held to share information and to plan the investigation. The prime agencies who must attend are health, social services and police. (The initial police contact for any case arising at Anytown District Hospital is the Detective Inspector at Anytown.) All decisions made at the strategy meeting should be formally recorded and 'signed up to' by each agency.

3. From the outset an atmosphere of secrecy must prevail, and knowledge of any (potential) investigation must be confined to the smallest possible group. Any reference to suspicions in the patient's files, etc must be carefully managed. A suspected perpetrator must not be confronted or alerted to a proposed investigation unless this course of action is agreed by the multiagency team.

4. If the suspicion is that acts are being carried out that amount to criminal offences – for example assault, poisoning, damage to feeding tubes – the police will bear the main responsibility for the gathering of evidence.

5. A decision to use technical or covert equipment to gather evidence must not be taken lightly. Due regard must be given to the rights and privacy of the suspect, and to the risk of breaking down the doctor/parent relationship to the detriment of the child's care. Other, more conventional methods, should first be tried or deemed to be impractical before this step is taken.

6. Any technical devices other than medical equipment used to gather evidence will be supplied and managed by the police in order that the highest standard and quality is achieved. Likewise, any monitoring of such equipment which may be required will be carried out by police officers (with advice from medical staff where appropriate). In any case where it is considered desirable to use covert equipment owned or managed by the police, an officer of at least assistant chief constable rank will have to sanction its use. He or she will review thoroughly its necessity before granting authority.

7. The police must carry out any work in a hospital sensitively and delicately. There must be a great deal of understanding

about the considerations and concerns of the other agencies. Any disruption to the normal life in a hospital must be kept to an absolute minimum and this may particularly apply if a suspect has to be arrested on hospital premises.

8. The findings and conclusions of the investigation must be shared with the multiagency team so that every effort can be made to offer full protection to the child.

9. Experience has shown that full and frank recording in nursing/medical notes of unusual events is highly beneficial, but care must be taken if a suspect has access to such notes.

Legal orders

There are two ways under the Children Act 1989 whereby a child can be offered urgent protection from an abuser.

1. Under Section 46 a police officer can take a child into 'police protection'. This means that if he or she feels that a child is at risk of being subjected to significant harm, he or she can remove the child from an abuser or order that the child is not removed from a safe place, such as a hospital. This can be carried out immediately and with no recourse to the courts.

2. Under Section 44 anyone can apply to the court for an emergency protection order. If granted, this means that the child can be removed from home or retained in a safe place, such as a hospital. Emergency protection orders can be challenged within 72 hours and can last for up to eight days, with an extension to 15 days, by application in exceptional circumstances.

The management of the press and media is something that must be considered at an early stage. MSBP is a topical and newsworthy subject and a great deal of press and media interest can be expected. The press will undoubtedly try to find out if CVS has been used, as it seems to be the most controversial aspect of MSBP investigations. If CVS is employed and there are criminal court proceedings, its use must be disclosed to the defence. A 'public interest immunity' hearing in front of a judge is likely to fail because the use of such equipment has already been disclosed in some parts of the country. It may be extremely damaging if it became known locally that CVS has been used because for something to be 'covert', it obviously needs to be secret. Any decision to use it therefore must be weighed against the possibility of disclosure in court and the press. On a more general note, there should only be one media outlet, which should be decided upon at the initial strategy meeting.

Conclusion

The case studies highlighted different types of MSBP which were investigated in different ways. Mistakes were made by some people (including the police), but there are also examples of good practice and good inter-agency working, particularly in Case 3. The main lesson to be learnt from all the case studies is that an earlier referral and investigation would have saved the children from a lot of pain and possibly in one case, death. It therefore cannot be stressed strongly enough that the people and agencies involved in child care must talk to each other and share their concerns as soon as they have them, not when they are '90 per cent sure' (Meadow, 1989) that abuse is taking place.

Finally, the views and ideas expressed in this chapter are those of one police officer who happens to have been involved in several MSBP investigations. There is no attempt here to give the 'official' police view or to standardise procedures nationally. Each case, area and set of professionals is different, which is why it is important for those who may be involved in these investigations to decide for themselves the procedures that will best suit in the other local agencies.

References

Meadow, S R (1984) 'Fictitious illness – the hinterland of child abuse', *Recent Advances in Paediatrics*, pp217–232, Churchill Livingstone

Meadow, S R (ed.) (1989) *The ABC of Child Abuse*, British Medical Journal

Rosenberg, D A (1987) 'Web of Deceit,' *Child Abuse and Neglect*, 2, 547–563

9. Balancing acts: a family court perspective on Munchausen syndrome by proxy

Anna Markowycz, The Children's Society Guardian ad litem Project, Hull

Background information in relation to care proceedings

The Children Act 1989 provides the legislative framework within which the pertinent issues in respect of a diagnosis of Munchausen syndrome by proxy (MSBP) are ruled upon by the court. The decision to instigate court proceedings is usually influenced by the need to protect the welfare and interests of the child. By that stage there is, almost inevitably, a conflict between the local authority and the other interested parties, such as parents and other family members, as to how the protection of the child can best be undertaken. Key features in the process will have been the contribution of medical opinion(s) and the social services' knowledge of the child and family.

At the outset, the court must decide what factors constitute significant harm in relation to an allegation of MSBP abuse. Generally, the existence or likelihood of significant harm and its attributability within the immediate environment of the child, are key components in the criteria for the making of court orders providing for the compulsory intervention by the local authority in the care and upbringing of children. The Children Act does not provide a definition of the term 'significant harm', but Section 31 requires the court to be satisfied that certain threshold criteria exist. Thus, in Section 31(9), 'harm' is defined as 'ill treatment or the impairment of health or development' of a child. Furthermore, ill treatment includes sexual harm and forms of harm that are not physical, thereby including some forms of emotional harm. Impairment of health is defined as mental or physical health; and impairment of development is described as physical, intellectual, emotional, social or behavioural development. The significant harm test also requires the court to consider whether any harm suffered by the child is attributable to the parent or other carer whose lack of care caused the harm. The fact that the threshold criteria are essentially met does not mean that the court has to make an order.

In relation to the significant harm test, it is useful to consider the case of Re: M (A Minor) (Care Orders: Threshold Conditions) (1994) 3 WLR 558 (HL) in which the question arose as to the time period to which the words '...is suffering...significant harm' relates. On appeal, the House of Lords decision indicated that the relevant time for considering whether the threshold criteria are met is the date when the local authority put in place arrangements for the protection of the child, provided such arrangements were still in place at the date of the trial. In most cases, therefore, the relevant date would be the date of the application for the care order. In cases where the need for such arrangements had ceased by the date of the hearing, however, it is not permissible to look at any date before this. Consequently, it is necessary for practitioners to bear in mind that any change of circumstances prior to a final hearing may have a major impact in establishing the date upon which the threshold criteria must be satisfied.

In each case where MSBP is alleged, the court is charged with the responsibility of safeguarding the welfare and interests of the child. The court will determine the issues placed before it on a balance of probabilities. For example, in the process of adjudicating upon complex and conflicting information, medical or otherwise, the court will need to balance whether it is more probable than not that what is said to have happened in accounts of a particular incident, by professionals and lay people alike, did happen. The balancing principle similarly applies to the area of attempting to measure any future likely risks to a child. Although child care cases should ideally be conducted in the spirit of 'inquiry', it is almost inevitable that most parents, family members and professionals unfamiliar with court proceedings and protocol believe otherwise. In the final analysis, the court will give more weight to one party than another.

Role of the guardian ad litem

The provision to appoint guardians ad litem (GALs) in certain court proceedings is found in S41(1) of the Children Act. They are appointed by the court and their primary duty is to safeguard the welfare and interests of the child during the course of the court proceedings.

In addition to contributing to the appropriate timetabling of proceedings, GALs provide an independent assessment of the child's circumstances, including their wishes and feelings. Consequently, GALs seek to contact or interview such persons as they think appropriate or as the court directs, inspect social services' records/documents and obtain such professional assistance as is considered appropriate in relation to safeguarding the child's welfare and interests. At the conclusion of their investigations, a written report is produced by the GAL which is available to all parties in the proceedings. The GAL is available for cross-examination about any oral or written evidence tendered to the court. At the conclusion of a hearing, at an interim or final stage, the GAL considers the possibility for appeal insofar as it is relevant to the interest of the child.

The use of experts in care proceedings relating to MSBP

In the light of limited current knowledge and research, a diagnosis of MSBP, alleged or otherwise, readily lends itself to a series of complex assessments within the court proceedings. The range of expert witnesses varies, but at the very least usually includes paediatricians and psychiatrists, both disciplines having their own fields of specialist knowledge. Social work assessments, normally undertaken by local authority social workers or voluntary child care agencies, are also an integral part of any assessment process involving the child and their family. These assessments, with a local authority care plan, are expected to be available to the court. The number of experts in any one MSBP case could, theoretically, be extensive. Judicial guidance is available concerning the instructions of experts and the use of experts in public law proceedings.

In Re: M (Minors) (Care Proceedings: Child's Wishes) (Family Division; Wall J; 2 December 1993) (1994) 1 FLR 749, His Lordship, Mr Justice Wall commented that it was essential for medical experts to be fully instructed. The context in which the expert's opinion is sought and the specific questions to be addressed are to be set out in a letter of instruction. Furthermore, that letter should be disclosed to the other parties and included in the court bundle. The guidance also requires all the roles, records, photographs, correspondence, X-rays and other relevant documentation held by doctors with previous clinical experience of the child to be made available.

Further guidance is provided in the case of Re: G (Minors) (Expert Witnesses) (Family Division; Wall J; March 1994) (1994)

2 FLR 291. In the course of protracted care proceedings with respect to a child victim of MSBP, the mother of the child concerned was granted leave to disclose medical records to 'experts'; her intention to instruct six experts – two adult consultant psychiatrists, a consultant child psychiatrist, two paediatricians and a consultant in paediatric biochemistry – was unknown to the court at the time that the order was made. The reports of the mother's experts arrived late (one arrived on the second day of the hearing) and caused delay in the preparation of the case by the other parties.

The above case adds weight to the view that a generalised order permitting a party in the proceedings to show documents to 'experts' should no longer be acceptable in practice. In giving leave, it is the court's duty to exercise control over the evidence that it permits to be adduced before it, in the interests of justice, of the child(ren) with whom it is concerned and of the public, in order to ensure that public funds are not wasted on unnecessary investigations. Every order granting leave should either identify the expert or define the area of expertise in respect of which leave is given. Sir Nicholas Wall offered further guidelines which are included in Appendix 1.

In the case of Re: AB (A Minor) (Role of Medical Expert) (Family Division; Wall J; 1 July 1994) (1995) 1 FLR 181, Sir Nicholas Wall found that a child had suffered non-accidental injury; the following guidance on medical expert testimony in care proceedings was provided.

'1. Judicial findings of abuse can rarely, if ever, be made in isolation and on medical evidence alone: the factual substratum from which the allegations of abuse arise is usually of critical importance in an overall assessment of the case.

2. The expert forms an assessment and expresses his opinion within the particular area of his expertise. The judge decides particular issues in individual cases. It is not for the judge to become involved in medical controversy, except in the extremely rare case where such a controversy is, itself, an issue in the case, and a judicial assessment of it becomes necessary for the proper resolution of the proceedings.

3. Where an expert advances a hypothesis which is controversial within the medical profession, he must explain to the court that this is so, and put before it all the material which contradicts the hypothesis. The expert must also make all his own material available to the other experts in the case.

4. Parental denial is a commonplace of child abuse: to overcome that

denial and to accept responsibility for abuse which has in fact occurred is correspondingly painful and difficult for the parent. It is, however, a highly important factor in the consideration of the issue of child protection. Accordingly, if the medical evidence points overwhelmingly to non-accidental injury, an expert who advises the parents and the court that the injury has an alternative and innocent causation has in my judgement a heavy duty upon him to ensure that he has considered carefully all the available material and is, moreover, expressing an opinion which takes that material fully into account and which can be objectively justified.'

In the case of Re: C (Expert Evidence Disclosure Practice) (Family Division; Cazalet J; 21 November 1994) (1995) 1 FLR 204, His Lordship's guidance identified significant differences between the role of the expert in family cases and in other civil litigation. These can be found in Appendix 2. The case makes it clear that there is now a far more extensive duty of disclosure and of investigation to see whether there is material that should be disclosed than had previously been thought. The duties imposed upon experts and other professionals have been greatly extended; it is hoped that they will be prepared to adapt their practices in the way the guidelines now require. These appear to be consistent with promoting and safeguarding the welfare and interests of the child.

The availability of any expert and professional assessments should assist the court in identifying the existence of significant harm or the likelihood of significant harm where a diagnosis or suspicion of MSBP exists for the child. In order for the court to determine whether or not an order is required to protect the child, information needs to be available in respect of treatment outcomes for the identified carers of the child if they are the alleged perpetrator of MSBP, their partner or members of the child's extended family. It is also helpful to attempt to evaluate the likely impact upon the child's development, at all levels, of the identified treatment outcomes of the adult(s).

Other factors that influence proceedings in cases of MSBP

The sensitive management of a definitive, or otherwise, diagnosis of MSBP by both the social services department and health professionals is likely to be significant in influencing any party's decisions as to whether they contest court hearings, be they at the interim or final stages of the proceedings. Similarly, the adverse publicity surrounding the Beverley Allitt case (1994) and the fact that MSBP is associated with this, along with the reporting of extreme cases, need to be borne in mind. A range of dysfunctional behaviours, from induced symptoms at one end to exaggerated symptoms at the other, have been identified as being within the spectrum of the MSBP diagnosis. The classification and interpretation continues to be a matter for debate within and outside the medical profession. In the absence of any medical and professional consensus as to what constitutes MSBP abuse and acceptable levels of risks for children, the court will determine upon the issues accordingly, in relation to a perpetrator's treatment, encompassing the information identified in preceding paragraphs. The remainder of this chapter attempts to identify the information and sources of evidence that are required to satisfy the court that the threshold criteria conditions of 'significant harm' are met and that orders are necessary to safeguard the children's interests. They also reveal the variety and complexity of the range of orders available to the court.

Case 1

Child A was four weeks old when she was admitted to hospital via a referral from her general practitioner. Her mother was aged 25 years and her father 20. The parents were not married but had been living together for two years prior to their daughter's birth; she was their first child. Support was said to be available to these parents from both the maternal and paternal extended families.

On admission to hospital, the child appeared to be experiencing difficulties with her feeds, was vomiting and failing to thrive. Community midwifery staff had noted feeding difficulties with the child during their visits to the family home. During the first four weeks of her hospital admission, the child continued to experience symptoms of vomiting and diarrhoea, the cause of which remained unknown to medical staff, even after exhaustive tests. The child's failure to thrive within a hospital setting with no apparent physiological explanations concerned the consultant paediatrician. He suggested to the child's mother that she went home for 24 hours to see how the child fed and to enable the mother to have a good rest; she had been resident on the hospital ward with her daughter almost continuously since the child's admission. In the mother's absence, the child progressed satisfactorily, after which the consultant paediatrician began to suspect the child's condition was due to maternal MSBP. He confronted the mother with his suspicions; they were strenuously denied by both her and, subsequently, her partner.

On the second and fourth day after the paediatrician's confrontation with the child's mother, there was a significant deterioration in the child's condition. Her sodium levels were found to be excessively high and life-threatening. The child's health status was the result of interference by the mother with two bottle feeds stored in the ward's refrigerator; she had administered salt into these feeds, a course of action she denied.

Approximately three weeks after the initial confrontation between the consultant paediatrician and the child's mother, the matter was heard at the county court. The case had been transferred immediately to the higher court with the consent of all parties, as the transfer criteria regulated by the Children Act 1989 were deemed to have been satisfied.

After a three-day contested hearing, the court made the child the subject of an interim care order. It was renewed by consent up to the final hearing. The court further directed that supervised contact between parents and child be extended to a minimum of four hours per day in order not to pre-empt the issue of rehabilitation. In relation to medical assessments, the court directed that the mother and child be assessed by the appropriate consultants: that is, those with knowledge and expertise in the diagnosis, treatment and management of a suspected perpetrator of MSBP abuse. The experts instructed involved a further consultant paediatrician, a consultant child and family psychiatrist, a consultant adult clinical psychologist and a consultant forensic psychiatrist.

Following the interim hearing, the child was discharged from hospital to foster carers; she was joined by her mother, for the purposes of a residential assessment, approximately nine weeks later. Although opposed by the parents, a care order was granted at the final hearing. The care plan – adoption for the child outside the maternal and external family – was also endorsed by the court. During the course of the civil proceedings, concurrent criminal proceedings were instituted in relation the child's mother. At that crown court hearing she pleaded guilty and was made the subject of a probation order with a condition of treatment.

Case 2
Child B was aged approximately five and a half months when he came to the attention of the hospital social work department. His father was 25 years old and his mother 22. The couple had lived together for one year prior to the birth of their son. Their relationship was volatile and included several separations, with the child and mother leaving the family home on such occasions. The father had two children, aged four and two years, from a previous relationship although he had not lived with their mother as a family unit. These children had not come to the attention of the social services department.

General concerns were expressed about the number of hospital admissions (eight) accorded to child B since his birth. The presenting symptoms included milk allergy, vomiting, diarrhoea, feeding problems, choking, cyanosis, fitting and retention of urine. On most occasions, no evidence of these symptoms was present on examination. Visits to the child's general practitioner were also described as excessive at this stage of his development.

Two hospital admissions, in particular, appeared to cause the consultant paediatrician most concern. The first involved a series of examinations of the child by the general practitioner, clinical medical officer and the doctor at the accident and emergency department of the local hospital on the same day; his symptoms apparently increased in severity on each examination.

The second hospital admission involved the removal of a birthmark on the child's scrotum. The nature of the presenting symptoms offered by the mother was queried, with hindsight, by the consultant paediatrician rather than the paediatric surgeon who performed the surgical procedure. The child's maternal grandfather also informed professionals that the mother had had a fixation with seeing doctors and attending hospital with fictitious illnesses and symptoms since her teenage years. When asked, he believed the fixation had now transferred from the mother to his grandchild.

In this case, the local authority initially referred the mother to the local psychiatric service with a view to seeking an appropriate multi-disciplinary residential unit for mother and child. On examination of the mother at her home, the psychiatrist admitted the child's mother to a local unit as a voluntary patient, for possible post-natal depression. The admission was for 24 hours and was ended by the intervention of the child's maternal grandfather. Furthermore, the diagnosis of MSBP was not supported by the psychiatrist.

The conflicting paediatric and psychiatric medical opinions in relation to a diagnosis of MSBP influenced the local authority's decision to institute court proceedings. Throughout this six-month period the child had remained at home with his parents. A core group of professionals, which included the key social worker, community health visitor, community psychiatric nurse and the general practitioner, had monitored the child and mother's contact with the health and medical services within the community and hospital settings. The monitoring mechanism appeared to contain the mother's health-seeking behaviour in relation to the child to a more acceptable level. Consequently, at the first court hearing of the local authority's application, an application for an interim supervision order was supported by all the parties to the proceedings. On various applications, during the subsequent months, the court acceded to requests for medical expert assessments from a consultant paediatrician and consultant child and family psychiatrist from outside the local area, a consultant clinical adult psychologist and a consultant forensic psychiatrist. Both parents agreed to cooperate with the relevant experts.

Eighteen months after the concerns of the consultant paediatrician were first identified, final orders, by consent, were made by the court. In order to secure the child's future protection and living arrangements, a residence order was made specifically to the child's father. A supervision order for 12 months was agreed on the understanding that social services would seek an extension of the time period at its expiry, should it be deemed necessary on the child's behalf. Finally, the child's mother was prohibited from presenting the child for medical treatment without the prior approval of the child's father, for a period of two years except in the event of a medical emergency, under a prohibited steps order. The time period of this order coincided with the child's entry into the school system where, it was felt, his health could be monitored under alternative arrangements.

Case 3

This case involved two children, a sister, C, aged just under two years and a brother, D, aged three and a half years. The mother was approximately 23 years old and the father 30 when child C first came to the attention of the social services department.

The children's mother was the youngest daughter in a family of three; her two older brothers were in their mid-30s, married and with families of their own. As a result of her father's contractual employment, the children's mother was born and lived abroad for 11 years, thereafter mainly being in the day-to-day care of her maternal grandmother in the UK. The children's father was an only child. The parents shared similar family values and culture in relation to children, whereby mothers assumed the lead responsibility for providing the day-to-day care for the children. In this case, some extended members had links with the nursing profession and hospital administration.

The couple were living together at the time. They had known each other since the children's mother was 16 years old and had been married for five years. The parents had been separated, however, for about two months at the point when the family were first told of the MSBP diagnosis.

Between the ages of six and nine months, child C had been seriously ill in hospital, an experience that had been distressing for the child, parents, her brother and extended family members alike. The nature of the paediatrician's initial concerns, however, involved events prior to child C's second birthday. The mother reported that her daughter was experiencing breathing difficulties, having 'do's' in the night with associated choking sounds on some of these occasions. The child was also reported as having a nocturnal cough but was otherwise well during the day time. Her symptoms did not respond to the interventions of the general practitioner and the child was referred to the local paediatric unit. Although apparently advised to do so, the child's mother chose not to attend the hospital immediately. That same evening the child's condition was reported to have deteriorated. She was escorted to the hospital by her mother and a maternal aunt. The paediatrician referred the child to a specialist paediatric unit in another health trust the following day and she was moved there immediately. At that hospital, physiological recordings monitoring and tests, undertaken at varying times during the day, were inconclusive or negative.

During this hospital admission the consultant paediatrician formed the view that one explanation of the child's presentation could be that her mother was elaborating or distorting her account of the child's symptoms, if not inventing them and might, at worst, be provoking them. Social services were alerted at this stage. A core group of professionals was set up, involving health visitors, representatives of the paediatric departments of two hospitals, the family's general practitioner and the social work departments of two hospitals. Their task was covertly to monitor and investigate the children's and family's circumstances, unknown to the parents.

The child was discharged home to the care of her mother with physiological recording equipment designed for use at home and incorporating a low oxygen alarm. The paediatricians suspected the mother to be a perpetrator of alleged MSBP abuse. Some time after child C's discharge from hospital, her father made arrangements to see the consultant paediatrician. The mother had provided him with a list of health findings relating to their daughter which caused him considerable concern and for which he sought clarification. At that meeting the consultant paediatrician was able to confirm there was no validity in the contents of the reported health findings by the mother to the father. The child's father agreed to the continuation of the home recording equipment but was not made aware of the paediatrician's suspicions in relation to the mother.

After the meeting, the medical concerns were apparently heightened rather than reduced. Two separate incidents of alleged unrousability involving child C were subsequently reported by the mother to health professionals. In addition to these incidents, the consultant paediatrician was also concerned about some of the readings from the physiological recording equipment and could not discount the possibility that it had been interfered with by the mother. Arrangements were therefore made for child C to be admitted to the paediatric unit outside her geographical area. That stay was to involve the covert video surveillance (CVS) of mother and child.

Almost at the onset of CVS, the child's mother gave a series of descriptions of various health incidents relating to child C to a number of medical personnel. They dramatically demonstrated how the mother varied her accounts of incidents, successively introducing further components at the recounting of the same incidents.

Some degree of confrontation between the child's mother and the consultant paediatrician occurred during the CVS. On that occasion he shared with the mother some factitious information: namely that her local paediatric unit was of the view that there did not seem to be anything wrong with child C. He indicated there was pressure from the hospital for the use of its facilities, they were worried about the reported choking and vomiting and hoped the physiological recording equipment would be able to monitor such an incident. The aim of this 'partial' confrontation was clearly to prompt the mother into some form of action.

The child was later involved in an incident. The sequence commenced when she stirred in her sleep and concluded with the alarms of the recording equipment being activated requiring the attendance of nursing staff. Various exaggerated and inaccurate reportings of the incident were subsequently described by the mother to a number of people. The consultant paediatricians concluded that child C was a victim of MSBP abuse and that her mother directly caused symptoms of illness in child C, which led to her being subjected to unnecessary medical investigations, treatment and hospitalisation.

The child was returned to her local paediatric unit. At this point the diagnosis of alleged MSBP abuse was based at the most severe end of the spectrum of behaviour: that is, possible induced illness, much of that information being derived from technical evidence concerning the use of monitoring equipment within the home and hospital and from the use of CVS. The mother denied the allegations and appeared to be supported by the father. In view of the serious nature of the allegations, care proceedings were instituted by the local authority in respect of both children. At that point child D was staying with his father for a pre-arranged holiday and child C had been accommodated, with parental agreement, with foster carers.

On hearing oral evidence from one consultant paediatrician, the court was satisfied that the threshold criteria were made out for both children. The interim care orders were unopposed by either of the parents who were concerned that brother and sister be reunited, a course of action that was supported by the local authority. At the interim hearing it was also agreed that contact between children and mother was to be supervised, at a reasonable level and at the discretion of the local authority. In addition, leave was granted for the mother to instruct a consultant paediatrician. At the GAL's suggestion, both parents agreed to be examined by a consultant forensic psychiatrist at that stage. The mother subsequently withdrew her consent to the suggestion. In due course the court ordered that further copies and transcripts of the CVS tapes be made available in order to minimise delays, having regard to the number of experts that were instructed by the parties.

The renewal of the interim care orders was unopposed pending the outcome of a final hearing. After due consideration of the contents of the additional paediatric report and further enquiries, the GAL was granted leave to instruct a paediatrician on the children's behalf. On application by the mother, the case was later transferred to the High Court, a course of action that was supported by all parties. Shortly before the final hearing, the court granted leave to the mother for her to instruct a consultant clinical physiologist in order that he might report on the physiological monitoring of child C. A statement from a consultant ear, nose and throat surgeon was also permitted to be filed. Further application by the GAL for the children to be examined by a child psychologist was refused. However, leave was granted for a report to be prepared on the basis that the psychologist be permitted sight of the papers filed with the court.

The final hearing at the High Court commenced approximately 12 months after the initial concerns had been identified. During the final hearing the original diagnosis of MSBP, based upon possible induced illness of child C by the mother, could not be sustained and, in effect, the local authority's application was conducted on the basis that reported symptoms and incidents involving primarily child C, but also child D on occasions, were fabricated and/or exaggerated on the mother's part. The major focus of the hearing therefore concentrated on the extent, if any, to which this occurred, an exploration as to why it may have occurred and the possible implications of inaccurate reporting of health matters by the mother upon the future health and welfare of the children. The final hearing lasted almost eight weeks and took place over a three-month period.

The children's father filed a belated residence application, indicating he wished to be formally considered as a permanent carer for them. Consequently, should the local authority application fail, the court was still charged with the responsibility of adjudicating upon future arrangements for the children but in private law proceedings. During the course of the proceedings, various applications were made, including a request for the children's mother to be examined by a forensic psychiatrist. It was granted by the court but subjected to time constraints within the existing hearing. Of further note was that at the completion of the court proceedings, child C had spent ten months (27 per cent of her life) and child D nine months (or 16.4 per cent of his life) with foster carers.

On the evidence placed before it, the court concluded that the mother's elaborations and inventions in relation to the health of the children had been purposeful and deliberate. The harm to child C was said to be that she had been subjected to investigation, hospitalisation and the unpleasant and limiting effects of monitoring equipment, both at home and in hospital, unnecessarily. Insofar as her brother was concerned, the court felt that there was abundant evidence to establish that he was unhappy and adversely affected by the periods his sister had spent in hospital prior to the commencement of care proceedings.

Child D was, effectively, deprived of his mother's care during these periods. In considering the future arrangements for the children, the court took the view that the mother was more likely than not to continue behaving in much the same way. It was felt that the availability of a core group of professionals, to control the mother's access to health care, only addressed the active danger to the children of unnecessary or inappropriate investigations and treatment. The court took the view that such arrangements, in this case, did not address the more insidious or long-term effects that living in a household with a fabricated/exaggerated culture – perhaps shared with other members of the wider family living in close proximity – might produce in the children.

The threshold criteria were deemed by the court to have been met and orders for the children were deemed appropriate in this instance. (The case of Re: M (A Minor) (Care Orders: Threshold Conditions (1994) was available by the conclusion of the case.) The children's father was granted residence orders for both of them. The court made the children subject to supervision orders for 12 months and ordered they have supervised, reasonable contact with the mother. This was to be at the discretion of the supervising officer in consultation with both parents and the local authority. A similar order was made providing contact between the children and the wider maternal family. A prohibited steps order was also made in respect of the mother in the following terms. Save for periods of contact previously authorised by the supervising officer, the mother was, without the consent of the court, prohibited from having any other contact with the children. Other court directions related to the obtaining of a transcript of the judgement and restrictions as to its circulation. The mother was permitted to disclose a copy to a 'therapist' she may consult in relation to future treatment. The local authority were similarly granted leave in relation to anyone the father and/or the children consulted for treatment and therapeutic assistance during and after their move from foster care to their father's home.

Conclusions from the case studies

Establishing significant harm

An analysis of the three case studies would suggest that in court proceedings involving an allegation of MSBP abuse, the significant harm test is likely to require a close examination of the alleged perpetrator's health-seeking behaviour, at least in respect of the child but preferably also for themselves. This should involve a methodical scrutiny of all their medical and hospital records. The task could be coordinated by paediatricians with the assistance of other medical colleagues, since it is onerous and time consuming.

It is not facilitated by current record keeping practices where information may be kept in different places. Alternative and more systematic procedures for record keeping may need to be devised where child protection issues are identified.

Assessment presented to the court

The issue of appropriate assessments is likely to come under closer examination, given the judicial guidance available in respect of the use of experts in child care proceedings. A paediatric assessment is a prerequisite. It would seem that in order to determine levels of risks and likely treatment outcomes for the alleged perpetrator and the impact of these upon the child, a psychiatric assessment could be of some assistance. That in itself is problematic, since the court cannot order compliance. However, when such information might be helpful to the court, opinions should be expressed about such decisions.

In MSBP abuse cases, risk assessments need not be the prerogative of psychiatry, although 'expert status' in the proceedings may carry more weight with the court. In the process of evaluating risk, a number of factors need to be borne in mind. These include the nature of the alleged perpetrator's health-seeking behaviour, how this manifests itself, its function for the perpetrator and its effects upon the child. Whichever specialism is identified, it would be helpful if the expert had some clinical experience of dealing with MSBP cases, some knowledge of the current research findings or was able to liaise and consult with those professionals who had such expertise and knowledge. The development of 'multi-disciplinary assessment teams' in relation to MSBP and child protection issues would be of particular value, with a coordinator to manage the gathering of information. (Readers are referred to Gretchen Precey's chapter which describes such a model.) It may be possible to incorporate such a task within social work assessments.

Immediate placement of children pending the final hearing

In two of the three case studies the children were removed from the day-to-day care of their parents. Unless it is clear at the outset, and it rarely is, that rehabilitation is not a feasible option, the local authority is required to provide a level of contact between a child and an alleged perpetrator that does not predetermine this issue prior to a final hearing. The resource implications where contact requires supervision are extensive, particularly for babies and young children, if the bonding and attachment processes are not to be permanently impaired. The role of the supervisor needs to be clear, particularly as the content and process of contact should be an integral part of any social work assessment that evaluates the dynamics and functioning of adults and children. A child remaining with a perpetrator of MSBP is not free from risk; what needs to be determined on their behalf is whether the degree of risk is acceptable, a task that is difficult when looking at the potential impact upon a child's emotional and other development needs.

Use of CVS and other technical equipment

The use of CVS, which appears to have identified several MSBP abuse cases, has attracted much debate and publicity. Clearly, ethical considerations exist but it would appear there are some merits in its use. Again, extreme cases appear to be involved. Generally, the principle of working together in partnership with parents and families is very much supported by the court. CVS is clearly contrary to standard child protection and child care procedures, as an open exchange of information is not extended to parents and family members from the outset. The use of such covert procedures is not easily dismissed by the court in child care matters, as the protection of the child is of primary consideration. It is advisable, however, that where CVS is available, clear guidelines on procedures as to its use are laid out. Their absence is more likely to evoke criticism from the court than the use of CVS itself.

Much controversy has been reported in relation to the use and reliability of some technical recording equipment in MSBP abuse cases. It is not appropriate for the court to become involved in medical controversy except in the extremely rare cases where such controversy is, in itself, an issue in the case. In such circumstances a judicial finding would properly resolve the matter for that specific case. In Case 3 the court refused to be drawn into the medical controversy involving the technical equipment. Essentially, the court did not need to rely on any findings arising from its use in that particular case and thus made no ruling either way in relation to the technical monitoring equipment. Any controversies, including medical and professional ones, can readily detract from the child protection issues that merit serious consideration on behalf of the child.

Rehabilitation issues

All contested allegations of MSBP abuse that come into the court arena are likely to be subjected to a microscopic examination of all the evidence. It would also seem that the more intransigent the perpetrator's health-seeking behaviour is, the less likely it is that a court will take risks with the child and rehabilitation programmes. Should the prospect for change be favourable for the perpetrator and if it is consistent with the developmental needs of the child, then risks are more likely to be taken. In this respect, the practice of the court in MSBP cases appears to be consistent with the management of other hearings in relation to child abuse.

Placement with separated fathers

The court does appear to be receptive to the placing of children with fathers who are willing to assume primary responsibility for the care of the child and have a grasp of the issues on their behalf. In the case of unmarried fathers, their role in a child's life and functioning as a single parent need to be evaluated quickly in order that any issues regarding parental responsibility and placement can be resolved.

Use of Section 8 orders by the court

Disputes between experts in respect of areas of concern, diagnosis, risks for children and treatment outcomes will be ruled upon by the court where it is appropriate to do so. As Cases 2 and 3 demonstrate, utilising a number of Section 8 orders is seen by the court as being able to promote appropriately the welfare and protection of the child. This minimum 'interventionist' approach places the onus of controlling the inappropriate health-seeking behaviour with the child's identified carer rather than the local authority, a course of action that may, or may not, suffice for the child's future satisfactory development.

Appendix I

Re: G (Minors) (Expert Witnesses) (Family Division; Wall J; 7 March 1994) 2 FLR 291

'...

(2) As part of the process of granting or refusing leave either for the child to be examined or for papers in the case to be shown to an expert the advocates have a positive duty to place all relevant information before the court and the court has a positive duty to inquire into that information and, in particular, into the following matters:
(a) the category of expert evidence which the party in question seeks to adduce;
(b) the relevance of the expert evidence sought to be adduced to the issues arising for decision in the case;

(c) whether or not the expert evidence can properly be obtained by the joint instruction of one expert by two or more of the parties;

(d) whether or not expert evidence in any given category may properly be adduced by only one party (for example by the guardian ad litem) or whether it is necessary for experts in the same discipline to be instructed by more than one party.

(3) Where the court exercises its discretion to grant leave for the papers to be shown to a particular expert (whether identified by name or by category of expertise) the court should invariably go on to give directions as to:

(a) the time-scale in which the evidence in question should be produced;

(b) the disclosure of any report written by an expert both to the parties and to the other experts in the case;

(c) discussions between experts following future disclosure of reports;

(d) the filing of further evidence by the experts or the parties stating the areas of agreement and disagreement between the experts.

(4) Where it is impractical to give directions under para (3) (above) at the time leave to disclose the papers is granted, the court should set a date for a further directions appointment at which the directions set out in para (3) can be given.

(5) Where it is necessary to consider the estimated length of hearing at a directions appointment, the number of expert witnesses and the likely length of their evidence should be carefully considered and the exercise which I have set out in Note: Re MD and TD (Minors) (Time Estimates) [1994] 2 FLR 336 undertaken.

(6) It is a commonplace of care cases for the local authority to wish at the outset to carry out an assessment. Where this occurs, the court should in my judgment adopt the following approach:

(a) it should specify the time in which the assessment is to be carried out and direct that evidence of the outcome of the assessment be filed by a given date;

(b) it should fix a directions appointment for a date immediately after the date fixed for the completion of the assessments to reassess the case and give further directions for a speedy trial;

(c) once the local authority assessment is available, immediate thought should be given at the directions appointment, following its disclosure, to the evidence (expert and otherwise) required to bring the case speedily and fairly to trial. Any directions for expert evidence should identify the areas of expertise for which leave is given and lay down a timetable as per para (6) (b) (above);

(d) where a date for the final trial can be fixed before the assessment is complete, that should be done. More commonly, however, it will only be possible to assess the likely length of a case once the initial assessment is complete and the issues in the case emerge.

APPENDIX 2

Re: C (Expert Evidence Disclosure Practice) (Family Division); Cazalet; 21 November 1994) (1995) 1 FLR 204

In addition to the guidelines outlined in the earlier case (Re: G (Minors) (Expert Witnesses), Cazalet added the following:

'(a) Before the directions hearing:

i) any party proposing to apply for leave to instruct an expert should supply to all other parties and file with the court a written explanation of the area of expertise of the proposed expert, together with reasons why it is submitted that the court should grant leave, such document to be filed with the court at least 10 days before the hearing at which the application is to be made;

ii) any party proposing to apply for leave to instruct an expert should contact the expert prior to the hearing of the leave application in order to ascertain the availability of the expert for the purpose of giving evidence at the substantive hearing.

b) The letter of instructions to the expert should require discussion with other experts in the same field instructed in the case; and the letter of instructions (with supporting documents) should be disclosed to all parties. If relevant issues of fact are in dispute, the expert should be asked to give an opinion on each alternative hypothesis.

c) It is desirable that a general coordinator (often the guardian ad litem or local authority) be appointed to collate the expert reports and prepare a schedule (based on the expert's statement of the areas of agreement and dispute) of the areas of agreement and disagreement.

d)   At the directions hearing the court should consider giving the following directions:

(i) each letter of instruction to an expert shall point out as a condition of instructing that expert that the expert will be expected to prepare, after discussion with the other experts concerned, a joint document setting out the areas of agreement and dispute between them.

(ii) each party shall provide a copy of the letter of instruction to each expert, together with a detailed list of all documents supplied to that expert, to all other parties within seven days of instructing such expert;

(iii) each party's legal adviser shall send a copy of the letter of instruction and list of documents provided by other parties to their own expert within seven days of receipt;

(iv) directions as to when the expert's reports shall be served;

(v) insofar as any expert may provide further oral or written advice which changes a significant aspect of any previous written report, the substance of that advice shall be disclosed forthwith in writing to all the other parties;

(vi) each party shall ensure that the expert instructed on his behalf shall provide a joint document setting out points of agreement and dispute with other experts (referred to in para (i) above)) to be served on the other parties by ... (date);

(vii) no letter served after the date set out in para (vi) (above) shall be admitted in evidence without the leave of the court;

(viii) at any application for leave pursuant to para (vii) (above) the legal advisers to the party making the application will be expected to show cause why they or their client should not pay the costs of the application;

(ix) the (local authority/guardian/solicitors) shall within ... days of receipt of all the experts' letters referred to in para (vi) (above) by ... (date) serve on the other parties and file with the court a schedule setting out an outline of the points of agreement and dispute which appear from the letters referred to in para (vi) above.

(3) A local authority should disclose all relevant documents in its possession not covered by public interest immunity (see Re A and Others (Minors) (Child Abuse: Guidelines) [1992] 1 FLR 439). In particular, the local authority should consider what documents it has in its possession which are relevant to the matters before the court; and it is under a duty to disclose in the interests of the child and of justice documents which might modify or cast doubt on its case.

(4) It is for the court alone to decide whether to authorise disclosure of documents covered by public interest immunity; but the local authority should draw the attention of the parties' advisers to the existence of such documents, and invite an application to the court, if appropriate.

(5) In all cases it is important that the local authority should inform the guardian ad litem of any matters of concern within the documents. If the guardian (in the course of access to the authority's papers authorised by Children Act 1989, s42) comes upon relevant documents not likely to be disclosed, the guardian should invite the local authority to make disclosure; and if it does not do so, the court's attention should be drawn to the matter.'

10. Munchausen syndrome by proxy: presenting evidence in court

Dr Terence Stephenson, Senior Lecturer in the Department of Child Health at the University of Nottingham and Honorary Consultant Paediatrician at University Hospital Nottingham and City Hospital Nottingham

Introduction

This chapter is in three parts. The first part deals with the particular difficulties of gathering and presenting evidence in cases on Munchausen syndrome by proxy (MSBP). The second part deals with practical advice on preparing written statements and giving oral evidence in court. This advice is therefore applicable not only to MSBP but to presenting evidence relating to child protection cases in general. The final section of this chapter deals with the particular role of the expert witness, as opposed to the witness to fact, and the expectations of such a witness.

Writing as a paediatrician, inevitably much of what I include in this chapter is directed at doctors. Nevertheless, the broad principles outlined in all three sections should apply to most professionals involved in child abuse work. There have been several previous articles which have given helpful general advice to medical practitioners about presenting evidence in court, although none deals specifically with MSBP (Rentoule and others, 1973; Taitz and King, 1986; Williams, 1993; Gulleford 1994).

Although this article is aimed primarily at paediatricians, there is rarely a single diagnostic test that can confirm MSBP. One example of such a test would be an investigation that showed that blood which was allegedly passed into the child's nappy was in fact not the baby's blood group. In the absence of such incontrovertible evidence, there is no substitute for a comprehensive paediatric, psychiatric (child and family) and social work assessment and the meeting together of these professionals to share their information and opinions. The advice to paediatricians in this chapter should therefore not be taken in isolation.

MSBP: collating the evidence

Most cases of suspected MSBP involve voluminous amounts of documentation. This is partly because the alleged perpetrator (usually the child's birth mother) and her children have often had frequent and multiple contacts with different doctors, different hospitals and indeed different social services departments. The amount of paperwork is further amplified by the fact that there may have been several hearings in court, each generating a new bundle of photocopied records, statements and expert opinions. Of course, a witness to fact need concern him or herself only with what they have been told, what they have observed and the results of any medical tests of which they have knowledge. However, medical practitioners are rarely allowed to escape as a mere witness of fact and will almost invariably be asked, at least to some degree, for their opinion in the interpretation of those facts. The paediatrician who is not claiming to have particular expertise in the field of MSBP will still be expected to form opinions commensurate with his or her specialist training and experience. On the other hand, expert witnesses in cases of alleged MSBP have no first-hand knowledge of the facts, not having been involved with the case personally, and must therefore derive their information from written records and from interviews with the alleged perpetrator and children. Therefore, before reaching a conclusion about whether these allegations do constitute MSBP, the author of that opinion should try to obtain, as a minimum, the documents listed in Table 7.

There are a number of potential pitfalls here. The child or parent may have moved geographically or changed general practitioner despite remaining in the same geographical area. There may have been consultations at a number of different hospitals (classic 'hospital shopping') both in the local geographical area and on visits outside the area. The child may be known by a number of different names, particularly if the mother is a single parent or if she has had children by a number of different fathers. The siblings may be known by a different surname from the index child. If the mother has had a past psychiatric history, these records may be particularly difficult to trace. She may have given a different name at the

Table 7   Written documents required

1. The child's general practitioner notes
2. The child's health visitor record
3. The child's hospital(s) records (including nursing and physiotherapy records)
4. The siblings' general practitioner notes
5. The siblings' health visitor records
6. The siblings' hospital(s) records (including nursing and physiotherapy records)
7. The mother's general practitioner records
8. The mother's hospital(s) records (including obstetric and psychiatric records)
9. All social services records, case conference minutes, police interview transcripts and so on
10. Any previous expert reports
11. Any other relevant 'shopping' (see text)

time of previous overdoses or psychiatric admissions and psychiatric records are often kept separate from general hospital notes. Psychiatrists, understandably, are particularly wary of breaching patient confidentiality and may be reluctant to release the mother's notes without good cause. The mother's consent is of course required for release of both her own notes and those of her children, unless a court order explicitly states that this should be done. The general practitioner and hospital records manager will want to see copies, or even the originals, of a parent's written consent before releasing these records.

While the children's and parents' medical records are clearly the domain of the medical or paediatric witness, other agencies may argue that social services minutes and police interviews play no part in the medical assessment. This is completely wrong. In order for a paediatrician to reach an opinion as to whether MSBP has occurred, it is vital that he or she has access to as much information as possible relating to the alleged perpetrator and the index children. Valuable health information may be contained in the records of other agencies and inconsistencies and exaggerations in interviews with other professionals may tend to corroborate apparent hyperbole and fantasising in the medical records. The paediatrician, however, must be careful that confidential information in the records of other agencies is not shared with the mother during any interview. The information can be included in the paediatrician's written report, just as all information should be available to the court. Finally, the phrase 'any other shopping' in Table 7 means any other written documentation that tends to show a propensity for the mother frequently to seek attention, counselling or advice from other services. Examples would be self-help groups, charities, counselling services and alternative thera-pists, particularly allergy specialists about restriction diets for the child.

MSBP: forming an opinion

There is a maxim in medicine that 'the history is 95 per cent of the diagnosis'. By the history, doctors mean all the information that is told to them by the patient or, in the case of children, usually by the parents. It is axiomatic in medicine that patients or their par-ents approach the doctor because they want help and therefore it is assumed that on the whole they tell the truth. Unfortunately in child protection cases truth cannot be assumed and, since fabrica-tion is the essence of MSBP, the history is extremely unreliable. Deprived of the reliability of the history, the doctor is forced to rely on examination of the child and various blood investigations and X-rays but it has already been emphasised that there is rarely a single diagnostic test of MSBP. Without the guidance towards the target that a history provides, these investigations tend to be mul-tiple in number and blunderbuss in their lack of specificity, thereby subjecting the child to further, albeit inadvertent, abuse. For the expert witness obtaining the history second-hand from the medical records, it is important to be aware that medical and nurs-ing records are not factual documents. This is true in two senses. The first is that the medical records will often be a precis of what the doctor has been told, often by the child's mother, and therefore will tend to perpetuate the fabrications and exaggerations in her story. The second is that, since at the time the doctor is not usually aware that the case will subsequently reach court, the records are not written with this in mind and it may be unclear in the medical notes whether statements reflect what the doctor has been told, are his or her own opinion, or are his or her own observations rather than reported comments.

It is important that a paediatrician does not approach a case with preconceived notions. In particular, expert witnesses must draw attention to alternative explanations for what appear super-ficially to be suspicious events. Every childhood illness that cannot be explained or diagnosed is not necessarily fabricated or induced. Every paediatrician will have experienced perplexing cases when the child's problems have defied textbook classification but the paediatrician breathes a sign of relief when the child recovers inexplicably. On the other hand, recurrent unexplained illnesses over several years are rare and provoke concern. It is helpful to remember to 'believe what you see rather than see what you believe'.

Whenever possible, a paediatrician asked to give an opinion about a case of MSBP should meet the mother and the child. The outcome of such a case may have a great impact on the subsequent life of mother and child and that alone seems justification for meeting with them. However, in some cases the mother may have already been interviewed by a whole host of people (general practitioners, hospital doctors, nurses, social workers, the police, lawyers, psychiatrists, clinical psychologists, guardian ad litem) and it may not be appropriate for the mother to be seen simply to salve the conscience of the medical expert who is making a damning conclusion. The opinion that there has or has not been MSBP may be obvious from the written material alone and it may not be necessary to subject mother and child to further travel and interview. There is also the danger that, in person, the mother may appear much more plausible than from the impersonal written records. Perpetrators of MSBP may have succeeded in their fraudulent behaviour partly because they have a credible personality or the ability to induce sympathy and the paediatrician must be aware of this when meeting them in person. Moreover, a further interview with yet another professional fascinated by the complexities of their child's case may simply be continuing to fulful their need for attention. If the mother is articulate, plausible and concerned, the well-meaning paediatrician may be drawn into her web of lies and deceit and may ultimately over-identify with the mother and become a crusading champion for her innocence. This is particularly likely if the paediatrician fails to understand the role of the expert witness (see below) and sees himself or herself as acting for the party who has instructed him or her.

There are a number of important tenets which may help the paediatrician reach an opinion as to whether MSBP has occurred or not. In cases of MSBP there may, of course, also be genuine events and illness in addition to fabricated or induced illness. A known physical illness that explains part of the symptoms is not uncommon and may be intertwined with the fictitious illness. Moreover, an earlier genuine illness may act as a paradigm for, or demonstrate the attraction of, later fictitious illness. Extreme illness exaggeration, rather than total fabrication or induction, has also been recognised as a variant of MSBP in children who have a genuine disease (Masterson and others, 1988). Because of this possible mixture of genuine and fictitious illness, it is important for paediatricians to keep uppermost in their minds that, while each incident may have an explanation, the overall picture is what is important. This requires a probabilistic approach; that is, the paediatrician may have to assess the likelihood of multiple rare incidents occurring, although each individual incident has a possible explanation. In some cases, statistical advice has been taken to compute the likelihood of various events having occurred, or the likelihood of events occurring repeatedly in the presence of only one person. A word of caution is required here. One must be guarded about reaching conclusions because illness episodes occur only in the presence of the mother, as a young child at home is almost continually in the presence of his mother and she would indeed be the most likely person to be near when an episode such as apnoea occurs. However, unless the mother is resident, this is not the case with recurrent events that occur while the child is in hospital and such events may provide much stronger evidence that fabrication or induction is occurring. The other aspects of reaching an opinion about alleged MSBP relate to the details of the medical presentation and the typical features of perpetrators in MSBP. This will not be duplicated here as these aspects have been dealt with elsewhere (Meadow, 1989; Meadow, 1990; Bools and others, 1994).

Children are accorded a central position under the Children Act 1989, following on from the Cleveland report in 1988: 'Professionals should always listen carefully to what the child has to say...the wishes of the child should be taken into consideration'. However, it would be wrong to conclude from this that children never lie. There have been cases reported previously where the child has become enmeshed in the mother's abnormal illness behaviour and children have been rehearsed by the parent in giving false histories of illness or false allegations of abuse. There is also some evidence in the psychological literature that children are more prone to suggestion than adults and that they may come ultimately to believe strongly in ideas that were originally suggested to them by adults.

Legal process

The court must find as to the facts in the case. In cases such as alleged MSBP, in which the history is often long and complex and the documentation weighty, the only person with a complete overview of the case may be a judge hearing the case in court. In addition, only the judge will have the opportunity of hearing the individuals involved give evidence in person and be cross-examined on the factual basis of their statements. The judge is therefore in a better position than a medical witness, or indeed any other single witness, to reach a conclusion as to the true facts of the case after having heard all the evidence. This may be an argument for involving medical experts later in the course of a court action in which MSBP is suspected or for deferring a final medical report until some of the evidence has been heard, so that the non-medical facts in the case can be established. For example, it is not within the remit of a medical expert witness to establish who made anonymous phone calls and there may be other expert witnesses in the case, for example telecommunications experts, who could give an opinion on this. Nevertheless, the source of anonymous telephone calls may be very material to the medical expert witness's opinion of whether false allegations have occurred and therefore whether MSBP has occurred. A second example would be as follows. A mother who has allegedly perpetrated MSBP may also be accused of having lied to other parents in hospital, of having lied to her employer or even her bank manager. If the court finds these to be true facts, this must influence what weight the medical expert can place on the mother's history in the medical records. Unfortunately, it is rarely possible for the medical expert to defer comment until after the facts have been established, although the expert's view is clearly contingent on those facts.

MSBP is not a disease in the classical sense but a pattern of abnormal behaviour. A judge (or a jury in a criminal trial), without medical training, may agree that such abnormal behaviour has occurred by asking themselves the question 'did these events occur or were they fabricated?' or 'were these illnesses genuine or were they induced?'. This requires an examination of the pattern of events, an assessment of their probability, and a temporal relationship with the individuals concerned, without necessarily understanding the motive or psychodynamics that lie behind this abnormal behaviour. Such a conclusion might be arrived at without necessarily even invoking the diagnosis of MSBP and such a conclusion does not require the behaviour to be shown to be premeditated, deliberate or for the mother to have insight. In essence, therefore, a diagnosis of MSBP by a paediatrician may provide medical precedent, apparent motive, a greater understanding of the abnormal behaviour, and clues as to future treatment and ultimate prognosis. However, an assessment of whether the mother's behaviour is abnormal and whether this is harming the child does not depend solely on a paediatrician making this diagnosis. Just as a judge may have to assess 'did these events occur or were they fabricated?' in a fraud trial, without being trained in accountancy, in some respects MSBP is better viewed not as a medical diagnosis which only a medical practitioner can make.

Preparing a written report

The information should be set out in the report using the format in Table 8.

Table 8 Written reports

(The pages should be numbered)
The date of the report
Name of child and date of birth
Your full name
Position
Qualifications
Experience
Requested by ....
Based on
   – personal experience
   – documents
   – other sources
Consent

Detailed account of the child's medical problems
Chronology
History ('what you are told') including therapy/interventions
Examination ('what you find')
   – be graphic
   – include photos/charts
   – the date of the examination

Opinion
Has MSBP occurred?
Mechanisms
The future: harm and prognosis

Conclusions
Signed, dated

A chronology is a detailed account of the child's medical problems in chronological order. It is wise never to take the chronology of other professionals at face value, as they may have a particular agenda and omit important facts. They may also make simple mistakes or oversights which may be extremely important in forming an opinion of the case. The history may be what has been told to the paediatrician writing the report by the mother herself at interview, or the history as recounted in the medical records. Likewise the examination may be by the author or recount the examination findings of others. In both cases it is important that it is explicit in the report, whether these are personal observations or derived from the medical notes. Description should always be graphic in the sense that 'a four-inch cut across the forearm' is more explicit for the lay person than 'a superficial laceration of the lateral aspect of the distal upper limb'. In stating whether it is believed that MSBP has occurred, it should be made clear why this is believed to be so. Sometimes it is helpful for the court if those features of the case that tend to support a diagnosis of MSBP are listed and, in a balanced fashion, those findings that tend to militate against this diagnosis are also pointed out. It is helpful for the court to have views on future management if the opinion that the child has suffered from MSBP is found to be a fact by the court.

The burden of proof

In the United Kingdom, court cases are either criminal proceedings or civil proceedings. Criminal proceedings are usually brought by the Crown Prosecution Service and occur in only approximately three per cent of cases that involve physical abuse of children. The likelihood of criminal proceedings is higher in MSBP cases, partly because allegations of suffocation or poisoning are extremely serious and partly because it may be perceived to be in the public interest. However, custodial sentences are unusual except in those rare cases where the perpetrator is male. Criminal proceedings are heard in front of a jury and the burden of proof required to reach a verdict of guilty is 'beyond all reasonable doubt'.

Civil proceedings may represent private law (for example where a patient sues a doctor for negligence) or public law (in the case of child protection, usually brought by the local authority). In all civil proceedings, the burden of proof used throughout the case is 'balance of probability'. Balance of probability can be interpreted as meaning 'it is more likely than not that MSBP occurred' and this is a more helpful statement than 'consistent with MSBP'. A recent case, however, has created some ambiguity over the phrase 'balance of probability'. In Re: M (A Minor) Justice Waite said, 'The more serious the allegation the more convincing was the evidence needed to tip the balance in respect of it'. This would appear to drive a coach and horses through the simplistic notion that balance of probability meant 'more likely than not' and that this burden of proof was uniform throughout all civil proceedings, irrespective of the seriousness of the matter.

A day at court: giving oral evidence

There have been several recent reviews of this subject (Kitchen, 1989; Gulleford, 1994; Simms, 1994; Thompson, 1994). All are agreed on the following general points which apply to all professional witnesses giving evidence in court.

The cornerstone of good oral evidence in court is in the preparation that is done beforehand. The witness who has familiarised himself or herself with the case and has researched the relevant literature is much more impressive, and useful to the court, than a witness who constantly leafs through the papers as if he or she has never encountered them before. Furthermore, no matter how much preparation has been done previously, often a lengthy time elapses between the submission of a written report and actually giving oral evidence. Therefore, it is well worth reading the documents again and rehearsing the arguments the day before attending court.

Different people have different views about dress code. Many would argue that the reliability and authority of the expert's testimony should not be dependent on how he or she dresses. However, judges are on the whole conservative people and, given that the child's future may depend at least in part on the evidence, the future of such a child should not be prejudiced by a witness whose appearance is at odds with the gravity of the court setting.

A witness should arrive at court early, as counsel may wish to discuss the case before evidence is given. Counsel is not allowed to lead the witness but discussion beforehand may help clarify areas of disagreement between experts and help counsel to focus on these issues.

Witnesses sometimes become concerned about the issue of confidentiality. In child protection cases, there is a professional duty to disclose any information thought to be relevant to the child's interest. Witnesses are not entitled to refuse to answer questions put to them on the basis of confidentiality.

Once in the witness box, and having taken the oath, it is important to talk to the judge (or the jury in a criminal trial) and **not** to the barrister. If necessary, the witness should turn to face the judge or jury and answers should be addressed to the judge, rather than the witness appearing to be locked in argument with the barrister. A 'good witness' is one who speaks loudly and clearly and uses plain language. Technical terms should always be explained.

Many witnesses are drawn into arguments with counsel, particularly during cross-examination, and the overall opinion of the witness may easily be lost in minutiae. This can be avoided by remembering the following four maxims. First, witnesses are probably more expert in their area than anyone else in court. Counsel may certainly be well briefed and may seem to have all the recent references from the literature but the witness is the expert in his or her field whereas the advocate is an expert in law. Second, the witness is there only to help the court; the witness is in the box **not** the dock and is there to help the judge reach decisions about complex medical matters, for which he or she is not trained. Third, opinions should be decided **before** the witness appears in the witness box. An aggressive counsel should not be allowed to make witnesses hedge or dilute what they truly believe to be their opinions. Fourth, a witness should not try to score points off the lawyer – the witness will inevitably lose.

Cross-examination can be particularly trying for a witness, because many witnesses are not used to having opinions challenged in such detail. The cross-examination can sometimes result in an expert arguing a particular case, but this is wrong; witnesses are independent experts, not 'hired guns' and should be prepared to accept the weaknesses of their arguments as well as emphasising the positive points (Carne, 1993). However, experts must know the limits of their expertise and confine themselves to their specialty. The witness should be prepared to say 'I don't know' or 'I know where I can find that out' or 'I need more time to consider or read this'. An expert who is unqualified to give advice on any matter must decline to do so (Stone, 1995). In giving a balanced view of their arguments, experts must also distinguish clearly between facts and opinions.

Finally, the expert is there to aid the court and constant 'stonewalling' or refusal to answer a hypothetical question does not assist judges in reaching their conclusions. On the other hand, witnesses have a duty to tell the truth as they see it. Barristers will sometimes use the 'yes/no' technique or hypothetical speculation to advance their own arguments. Witnesses cannot be interrupted in their answers if they do not wish to be and can appeal to the judge if this constantly happens. It is up to witnesses to summarise their evidence by trying to give an overview of the whole picture and what they believe on balance of probability is the case, rather than dwelling on a whole range of possibilities.

There is continuing debate about the role of the court under the Children Act 1989. Some argue that this role should be 'adjudicative', that is, the role of the court is simply to decide whether the threshold criteria for an order have been met or not. Others argue that courts should be more 'participative'; that is, they should decide not only whether the grounds for an order exist but also how the order should be implemented. These arguments are similar, although not identical, to those relating to whether courts should be 'adversarial' or 'inquisitorial'. Criminal proceedings may seem highly adversarial, heightened by media interest and the presence of a jury, but child protection proceedings in the family division of the civil courts are supposed to avoid this adversarial approach. These courts exist to seek out the truth and act in the best interests of the child and therefore the judge may frequently have questions of the professional witness or may interrupt counsel to clarify a point or to ask a supplementary question. Moreover, following the 'Oxfordshire case' there is now a mandatory disclosure of all expert reports that have been commissioned (Oxfordshire County Council versus M [1994]). This emphasises the inquisitorial nature of the proceedings and removes a burden from the conscience of a professional witness who gives an honest and adverse opinion to the client instructing him or her, only to find that the report never reaches the light of day and he or she is never called to give evidence in court. Similarly, the Oxfordshire case may limit the amount of 'shopping' around until a favourable report is found but, alternatively, it may simply mean that solicitors instruct only those experts whose opinions they can guess in advance from previous cases.

The role of the expert witness

Professionals may give evidence in court in two different guises. The professional may appear as a witness to fact if he or she has been personally involved in the case. However, most professionals will not be allowed to stop their evidence at a catalogue of events but will be expected to pass opinions commensurate with their seniority and expertise. Other professionals may be called to give expert evidence and, although they will have seen the documents and may indeed have met the parties involved, they will not personally have been responsible for handling the case.

Expert witnesses have special responsibilities and an important role in child protection proceedings and much has been written about their evidence. Sir George Jessel (Abingdon versus Ashton 1873) said 'I very much distrust expert evidence ... we constantly see persons instead of considering themselves witnesses, rather consider themselves the paid agents of the person who employed them'. A tension can develop between the role of the expert, which is to present an independent opinion, and the role of the lawyer instructing the expert, which is to ensure that the client's case is presented in the best possible light. The lawyer may seek to achieve this goal by artificially limiting the factual context with which the expert is presented (therefore the expert should always ask for access to all documents), by raising hypothetical scenarios which are extremely unlikely in practice, by not drawing attention to unfavourable information in a very large body of documentation, and by selective quotation of the expert's written opinion. The general role of expert witnesses has been set out in a recent case in the commercial court (National Justice Companiera Naviera SA [1993]) although the principles apply to all experts.

- Expert evidence should be independent and unbiased.
- Facts or assumptions on which the opinion are based should be stated as well as facts that could detract from the concluded opinion.
- If a question falls outside the expert's area of expertise or there is insufficient data on which to form an opinion, this should be stated.

It is wise to heed this advice, as negligent experts are not entirely immune from being sued, an area of the law that has been reviewed recently (Gilberthorpe, 1992; Stone, 1995).

The particular duties of experts in children's cases have also been reviewed recently, both by Sir Edward Cazalet (Re: J) and Sir Nicholas Wall (Re: AB, Re: M, Re: G, Re: DH). These judgements make the following points:

- The expert expresses his opinion within his field.
- The judge decides particular issues in individual cases.
- The judge is not an expert.'Outside the legal field, the court has no expertise and has to rely on the evidence of experts.'

In Re: AB (a minor) Sir Nicholas Wall made the following particular points.

> 'The judge brings to the enquiry forensic and analytical skills and has the unique advantage over the parties and the witnesses in the case that he or she alone is in a position to weigh all its multifarious facets ... It follows that the dependence of the court on the skill, knowledge and, above all, the professional and intellectual integrity of the expert witness cannot, in my judgement, be overemphasised.'

It is increasingly common for experts to be advised to confer pre-trial to limit the number of areas over which there is disagreement. The unnecessary investigation of medical issues is expensive both financially and in terms of court time. Moreover, an ill-prepared report which falsely exonerates a parent may be damaging in that it will reinforce the parents' reluctance to accept responsibility for what they have done. Re: AB was such a case and Sir Nicholas Wall broadly agreed with a recent article in *Archives of Disease in Childhood* which stated that 'a court is not a suitable forum in which to advance untested hypotheses' (Williams, 1993). Sir Nicholas Wall added,

'The expert who advances such a hypothesis owes a very heavy duty to explain to the court that what he is advancing is a hypothesis, that it is controversial (if it is) and to place before the court all the material which contradicts the hypothesis.'

Conclusion

Cases of MSBP are invariably complex. It is hoped that the advice given in this chapter on collating the evidence in such cases, on preparing written and oral evidence for court, and on the particular demands of the expert witness, will help professionals involved in such cases in formulating their opinions. If so, this will help the courts to best protect both children and their parents.

References

Bools, C N, Neale, B A and Meadow, S R (1994) 'Munchausen syndrome by proxy: a study of psychopathology', *Child Abuse and Neglect,* 18 (9), 773-788

Carne, S (1993) 'Experts not just hired guns', *The Lawyer,* page 21, 12 October

Gilberthorpe, J (1992) 'Experts at risk', *Journal of the Medical Defence Unit,* 3, 69

Gulleford, J (1994) 'Preparing medical experts for the courtroom', *British Medical Journal,* 309, 752-753, September 24

Kitchen, N (1989) 'Lack of court training hinders doctor's case', *Hospital Doctor,* p.12, 21 September

Materson, J, Dunworth, R and Williams, N (1988) 'Extreme illness exaggeration in paediatric patients: a variant of Munchausen syndrome by proxy', *American Journal of Orthopsychiatry,* 58, 188-193

Meadow, S R (1989) 'Munchausen syndrome by proxy', *British Medical Journal,* 299, 248-250, July 22

Meadow, S R (1990) 'Suffocation, recurrent apnoea and sudden infant death', *Journal of Paediatrics,* 117 (6), 351-357

Medical Evidence (1981) guidance for doctors and lawyers published jointly by the Law Society and the British Medical Association London

Oxfordshire County Council versus M [1994] Fam.151 at 161 per Sir Stephen Brown P

Re: AB (A Minor) (Medical issues) [1995] 1 FLR 181

Re: DH (A Minor) (Care proceedings: evidence and orders) [1994] 2 FCR 3 at 47

Re: G (Minors) (Expert witnesses) [1994] 2 FLR 291 at 298

Re: J (Child abuse: expert evidence) [1991] FCR 193)

Re: M (A Minor) (Appeal) no.2 [1994] 1 FLR.59

Re: M (Minors) (Care proceedings: child's wishes) [1994] 1 FLR 749 at 758

Rentoule, E and Smith, H (1973) *'Glaister's medical jurisprudence and toxicology'*, 13th edition, pages 44-55. Churchill Livingstone

Simms, J (1994) 'Stand at ease in court', Healthcare Management, 24-26, February

Stone, J (1995) 'Immunity of the expert witness', *Journal of the Medical Defence Union,* 11 (1), 8-9, January

Taitz, L S and King, J (1986) 'Medical evidence in child abuse', *Archives of Disease in Childhood,* 61, 205-206

The National Justice Companiera Naviera SA versus Prudential Assurance Co. Ltd. 'Ikarian Reefer' (QBD [1993] 37 EG158)

Thompson, A (1994) 'Witness protection for doctors in court', *Hospital Doctor,* page 20, 17 November

Williams, C (1993) 'Expert evidence in cases of child abuse', *Archives of Disease in Childhood,* 68, 712-714

11. The treatment of children and their families where induced illness has been identified

Jenny Gray, former Social Work Team Manager, Great Ormond Street Hospital for Children

Arnon Bentovim, Child Psychiatrist

Peter Milla, Reader in Paediatric Gastroenterology, Great Ormond Street Hospital for Children

Introduction

The literature relating to Munchausen syndrome by proxy (MSBP) and in particular to the management and treatment of children in whom illness has been induced, has been written predominantly from a medical and to a lesser extent psychiatric perspective (Eminson and Postlethwaite, 1992; Meadow, 1977, 1982 and 1985; Rosenberg, 1987; Samuels and others, 1992; Southall and others, 1987; Waller, 1983). The social work literature is sparse (Manthei and others, 1988; Masterson and Wilson, 1987; Rees, 1987) and there are few references to considering the management of this type of child abuse within a child protection framework, although it is recognised as physical abuse in *Working Together* (Department of Health, 1991). The aetiology of the abuse tends to be conceptualised as a function of the mother's psychopathology rather than the family's characteristic way of operating. There are few studies of the long-term outcomes for children (Bools and others, 1992 and 1993; Rosenberg, 1987). With some exceptions (Neale and others, 1991; Waller, 1983), the main focus of the literature is on the identification and initial management of the abuse (Eminson and Postlethwaite, 1992; Masterson and Wilson, 1987; Meadow, 1985; Rees, 1987; Rosenberg, 1987; Samuels and others, 1992) rather than intervention or treatment from a family perspective (Griffith, 1988; Manthei and others, 1988). Yet family members must change the ways in which they care for and interact with the abused child and each other if the child is to be protected and healthy when living within their family context.

The authors have analysed the data relating to a sequential series of 41 cases of induced illness referred to one hospital child protection team for assistance with their management. Some of the main findings have been presented previously in abstract from (Gray and others, 1993; Gray and Bentovim, 1994). This chapter presents a summary of the features of four different types of presentation found and the relationship between the long-term management of this type of child abuse and the outcomes for the children and their families. The methods of intervention used in the cases of two children and their families are described in detail to illustrate how the quality of outcomes can be maximised for all family members.

Method

Among the 41 children in the sample there were 24 boys and 17 girls. At the time of identification, their ages ranged from four weeks to 14 years. As a consequence of identification of illness induction the children became the subject of child protection concerns.

A qualitative analysis was undertaken by reviewing the medical and social work notes of each child. In addition, at least one of the hospital staff who analysed the data had been involved in the management of each case and therefore held detailed clinical knowledge about them. The cases had been identified in the period from 1984 until 1991, during which time the team's methods of management had developed.

The definition of outcomes

For the purpose of this study, the following criteria were used to define a good outcome for the child:

- There were no further episodes of illness induction.
- If the child had any need for further medical treatment, this was given appropriately.
- The child's health and development milestones were met.
- The child was living in a protective environment.
- Either the required change had taken place in the family system or the child was placed in an alternative family situation.

The outcome was defined as poor if any of the above criteria were not met. If the child died and abuse had contributed to the death, the outcome was automatically rated as poor.

Findings

Four patterns of presentation

Analysis of the case records revealed four different patterns of presentation (Gray and others, 1993). It is important to recognise that the presentation of some children included the features of more than one pattern.

- The first pattern (ten cases) was characterised by severe failure to thrive and the active withholding of food from the child by their primary caretaker. For example, a mother was observed by a member of the team to throw her child's food away while seeming to be feeding him.
- In the second (five cases) the child was also failing to thrive, but here there were accompanying allegations of severe allergies, usually to food, which led to extreme diets being given to the child, causing poor growth.
- In the third (15 cases) the parents alleged that their child had symptoms of a worrying nature – for example, stopping breathing or having fits, demanding extensive investigations to elucidate the cause.
- The fourth pattern (11 cases) consisted of children who had been given a substance such as salt or laxatives or where the parent was actively interfering with the child's medical treatment. There were no identified cases of smothering. Children about whom this was a particular concern were referred to another tertiary hospital for further investigation.

Numbers of children subject to a statutory order and/or on the child protection register

Of the 41 children in the sample, 19 had their names placed on the local authority's child protection register and 13 had been made the subject of either a care order or wardship (pre-Children Act 1989).

The outcomes for the children

At the point of review, four children had died, two at the time of identification. In the other two cases the causes of death were complex and induced illness was not the only factor. Of the remaining 37, 21 were found to have had poor outcomes and 16 to have had good ones (Gray and others, 1993).

Seventeen children from all of the patterns of presentation except the second, had presented in a life-threatening situation. The children's outcomes were not related to the type or severity of the illness induced in them but to the way in which their cases had been managed. The management of the following two contrasting cases resulted in good long-term outcomes for the children.

A description of the management of two cases

The initial identification and management of the cases was undertaken while the children were in-patients. Liaison with the relevant local social services department and health authority personnel, and any other professionals involved in the child and family members' lives occurred at an early stage. They became involved in the case as soon as this became appropriate within a child care and child protection framework. The hospital and relevant local authority's child protection procedures were followed. At times this meant that there were differences between the hospital's and local area child protection committee's procedures and practices which required resolution. In some cases a satisfactory accommodation could not be found and ultimate responsibility for the child protection management and intervention lay with the local authority social services department in which the child was deemed to be resident on discharge from hospital.

A case where the initial outcome was poor, but good in the long-term

The following case has an initial poor but subsequent good outcome. This was of a girl aged two and a half years, who was the younger of two children in the family (her brother was aged four). She presented in a life-threatening state with an exceptionally high sodium content in her blood which was subsequently found to be due to salt poisoning. She had a previous medical history of having sustained a fractured arm at four weeks, experienced feeding problems which required hospitalisation at eight months, and had sustained bruising to her head at 20 months. Objectively there seemed to have been a lack of protective action following what in retrospect seemed to have been abusive behaviour. Prior to her hospital admission, she had been seen at three different hospitals and was well known to her current general practitioner and health visitor.

Despite the gravity of the child's health situation, at the point of identification the mother seemed to be emotionally disengaged from her daughter. The father perceived her illness to be related to eating problems and his solution was that the children would require disciplining at meal-times following discharge: he did not seem to recognise the seriousness of his daughter's situation. The couple had a history of marital difficulties and the mother had a history of depression, unsubstantiated medical illnesses and conflicts with various members of the medical profession. The couple had experienced a number of difficulties in their parenting careers and their children were perceived as problems, with each parent having a different solution to these difficulties.

A careful review of the medical evidence indicated that the child had been poisoned with salt and had no other medical problems. Both parents denied administering salt and could not satisfactorily explain its presence especially in such large quantities. A comprehensive review of each family member's medical, psychiatric and social histories was undertaken and all information was verified. An initial social work assessment of the child and family's current situation was undertaken prior to the holding of an initial child protection conference where the children's names were placed on the child protection register. The local authority decided not to initiate any legal action nor to place the children out of the family. The conference plan was based on the children living with both parents and being regularly monitored by the local paediatrician for signs of poisoning. The mother was to be provided with dietetic advice, with particular reference to appropriate levels of salt intake for children. A psychiatric assessment of the family was planned. However, within one week both children were found to have excess salt levels in their blood. Following this re-abuse their grandparents initiated court action. The children were made wards of court with care and control to the local authority, and were placed with foster parents. They had contact with their father: their mother was admitted to a psychiatric unit and later was charged with harming the children and fraud (for other offences). Their mother later acknowledged poisoning both children after the conference because she felt that nothing had changed. The children thrived in their new placement and the long-term plan was to place them for adoption.

A feature of this case was the differences of opinion between professionals and agencies about the way in which the case was initially managed. This was most marked between hospital and community-based staff and agencies. Given the life-threatening nature of the type of abuse, the lack of acknowledgement by a parent of any responsibility for the poisoning, the professionals' lack of understanding of how the abuse occurred and therefore how to prevent further abuse and possible death of the child, the hospital's view was that both children should be made the subject of an interim care order and be placed with foster parents pending a comprehensive family assessment being undertaken. However, the child protection conference participants, in particular those from community health, believed that the protection plan was sufficient to prevent abuse reoccurring. Fortunately, following their return home, the level of poisoning was not high enough to cause loss of life or serious long-term impairment to health.

A case where both the initial and long-term outcomes were good

In the second case, throughout the process, the management was undertaken collaboratively between the hospital and local community agencies. This boy was aged five and a half years at the point of identification, although he had been known to the hospital from an early age. He was the youngest of three children: in infancy, his eldest brother had been placed on the child protection register because of parenting concerns and his middle brother had been seen at the hospital regarding cow's milk protein intolerance and hyperactivity, but was now well. This child had been investigated and treated for a number of different symptoms. Initially he was seen because of gastro-intestinal problems (there was also concern about his feeding and hearing): he was considered to be atopic, a condition he would outgrow. During a hospital admission at 23 months he was found to be functioning at a 14-17 month level in motor control and language. At the age of three and a half years his mother reported he had been having blank episodes for the last six months. An electro-encephalogram and brain scans were normal, but as his mother insisted he was having fits he was prescribed medication for epilepsy. His mother said his fits were preceded by bouts of hyperactivity and therefore he was seen regarding the possible relationship between food allergy and fits. An extremely complicated diet was tried with no improvement reported. At the age of five years he was prescribed chloral hydrate for sleep problems. Then for several months his mother reported he had episodes of extreme drowsiness which developed into unconscious episodes. When admitted to hospital in a severe coma there was concern about his survival, but he recovered before any cause could be ascertained.

While an in-patient, the attacks continued. Urine and blood samples taken during an attack indicated that one and a half times the therapeutic dose of chloral hydrate had been administered, although it was not being prescribed on the ward. The most likely explanation was that the drug was being given by a member of his family as the attacks only occurred when his mother was present on the ward (his father did not visit initially). The history of drowsiness in the morning was consistent with an excessive dose of chloral hydrate being given. In order to obtain an objective picture of the child's health, the consultant asked the mother to remain away from the hospital for two days. During this time the child was well. Following an outing from the ward with his parents he had another attack: pharmacological tests were negative. However, following another attack four days later (during an outing to the park with his mother) a further test showed the presence of unprescribed chloral hydrate in his system.

On admission, the mother said her son needed to wear a crash helmet to protect his head when he fell to the ground during attacks: he was taken to school in a push-chair because he had mobility problems. His mother treated him as a much younger child, encouraging him to remain in bed and to watch videos. She had asked medical staff on at least two occasions if he could be given a sedative to calm him down as she was embarrassed by his behaviour on the ward. This request was declined and the mother was reassured that his behaviour was not a problem. He had no problems sleeping at night. Despite reported allergies to certain foods, it was noted he showed no ill effects from eating prohibited foods to which he had illicitly gained access. In the absence of his mother he was an alert, active but immature child.

All medical findings being negative, the local social services department, who were already very involved in a supportive capacity, were advised of the hospital's concern that this child was being given a substance that was causing his unconscious episodes. A strategy meeting was planned as a consequence of receiving the positive pharmacological result. At this, significant information about the child and family was shared and analysed. From eight months previously, the child was reported to have been coming to school in an increasingly drowsy state, recovering by lunch-time, until he became too ill to attend. In response to his mother's request for help with his hyperactive behaviour, social services had provided respite care for the child on a regular basis: the care staff had not observed any of the symptoms or behaviours described by his mother. No fits had been witnessed by any community-based professional, despite them having seen the child frequently and for significant periods of time. It was also noted that the middle child had been presented with similar medical problems but was now well.

The mother had complained of her husband's lack of support

and, despite the relationship being close to breakdown, had declined offers of marital therapy. She had a long-standing psychiatric history (since her late teens) and had had periodic treatment for depression since the birth of her first child, now aged 18, which seemed to have been ineffective. The mother was reported to have experienced parenting difficulties with all her children and again therapeutic help did not seem to have been successful. She also had a very poor relationship with her own parents. Little was known about the father and indeed he had not visited his son in hospital until after his wife had been asked to stay away for two days. However, on the ward he also had wanted his son to be calm and had encouraged him to watch videos.

Despite all the factors that showed the child had been given unprescribed medication during the hospital admission, there was no evidence of who was responsible. The meeting decided that the parents would be told that their son had been found to have one and a half times the therapeutic dose of a drug that had not been prescribed on the ward and would be asked for an explanation of this finding. The consultant would not exclude the possibility of the child having some form of epilepsy, but would be clear that the picture of drowsiness in the mornings and unconscious episodes could be accounted for by excessive doses of chloral hydrate. The parents would be asked to agree to their son remaining in hospital for a week without being visited in order to monitor his health and behaviour; after this there was likely to be a period of supervised visiting, during which time efforts would be made to try and understand how the sedative came to be administered. The meeting agreed that a place of safety order (pre-Children Act) be sought if his parents attempted to discharge him against medical advice. A psychiatric assessment of the family would be proposed. In addition, the general practioner was to undertake an investigation of the amounts of chloral hydrate prescribed by the surgery: unbeknown to the hospital, the mother had had many repeat prescriptions of the drug and the previous week had asked for capsules for when her son 'came out of hospital'.

In response to the above, the mother said that she did not have any supplies of the drug and had not given any to her son for some time. The parents agreed to their son remaining in hospital. The following day, both parents saw the ward social worker and doctor. The mother said she had given her son the normal prescribed amount while on the ward because she wanted to calm him down as she was embarrassed by his hyperactivity: she said she had not wanted to harm him. The next day she made similar statements to the local social worker indicating she had also given him the drug while he was in the local hospital.

As a consequence of obtaining this information, the local social services department obtained a place of safety order and an initial child protection conference was set up. All family contact was supervised by a social worker and there were no further episodes of fainting or unconsciousness. In the interim period the child remained in hospital while an assessment of his medical, psychological and social situation was undertaken. His behaviour and development were monitored on the ward. In response to the parents' agreement, a psychiatric family assessment was commenced. The psychiatrist framed the abuse as the mother's attempt to manage her son while in a desperate emotional state and that it had been a cry (possibly unconscious) for help and support. Initially, the father was very confused and believed that a grave injustice was being done to his family. Within days he was accepting responsibility, saying that the events must have happened and the couple wanted to do everything necessary to ensure their son could return to the family. The mother continued to acknowledge that she had given the medication but could not remember any details.

At the conference, the child's name was placed on the child protection register and it was decided to seek a care order. Given that the child had presented in a life-threatening situation, the family had a history of not changing despite considerable therapeutic input, and the father's disengaged state, the conference participants were pessimistic about the parents' ability to meet their son's future needs. Thus the making of a care order protected the child, ensured he was living in a nurturing environment and impressed on his parents the seriousness of the concerns. It was considered necessary to ensure the family engaged in the child protection and therapeutic plans in a meaningful way. In practice the care order provided an incentive for the family to change. The police, who had previously interviewed the parents, were still considering whether to charge the mother. The conference members did not consider this would be helpful from a child care perspective and subsequently no action was taken.

The child protection plan required the child to be placed with foster parents with thrice-weekly supervised contact with his family. Therapeutically, a six-week psychiatric assessment was to be undertaken by staff in the hospital's day centre, after which time long-term plans could be made. A psychological assessment of the child's functioning informed direct work with the child.

The child's health was comprehensively assessed and he was

found to be functioning well physically but developmentally delayed and immature. He was involved in a very enmeshed relationship with his mother and behaved in a babyish manner when interacting with her. His mother found him a difficult child to manage. In the ward situation it was notable how different he was in her absence: he became a lively child interested in making friends and exploring everything in his surroundings.

The foster parents were introduced to the child while he was in hospital and ward staff explained his current medical situation: that he was a well child. This intervention was considered vital so that the foster parents were not confused by conflicting versions of his health and future medical needs.

The psychiatric assessment focused on the parents' perceptions of their son's health and developmental needs, their ways of interacting and managing their younger children, the mother's own psychiatric state and the parents' normal patterns of interacting with each other. Initial therapeutic work included enabling the parents to work together on marital and parenting issues, the mother to develop new and more functional methods of managing her children, both parents to interact with their son in an age-appropriate manner, and helping the mother make better use of the vast array of community support already being offered.

In this case all the other professionals who knew the family believed the evidence of abuse and indeed felt helped by having a clear statement of the child's medical situation and his needs. The staff at his school and at the centre providing respite care had been confused by the discrepancies between their observations and what the mother told them. All medication, special diets and unnecessary medical intervention were stopped. The health professionals treated him as a well child. Inappropriate services – for example, respite care at a specialist centre and financial help relating to a sick child – were withdrawn. The use of a buggy and crash helmet ceased. The child protection and therapeutic plans were understood and supported by all those involved with the family. The local social worker undertook a coordinating role of key worker and continued to be involved with the family, her involvement complementing that of staff at the hospital.

Following the period of initial assessment, all therapeutic work with the family was undertaken by the social worker. The foster parents and school staff were involved in helping the child learn age-appropriate ways of functioning. The family, working in partnership with the professionals, were able to change as a result of the therapeutic input – a significant achievement, given the long-term history of the mother not having changed despite extensive input and the father being totally disengaged from family issues. As a consequence the child was able to be rehabilitated home with both parents and to thrive.

In managing this case it was crucial for all professionals to maintain a child protection focus while providing therapeutic help to the family, engaging the father for the first time. The multi-agency team worked closely together, following a clearly defined child care plan. The mother's needs were addressed within this context but at all times those of her son remained paramount.

Discussion

In addition to a number of different teams at the hospital, several local authorities and health authorities were also involved in the management of these children. Therefore these cases were managed in a variety of different ways. An analysis of the findings demonstrated that the way in which the teams managed their initial suspicions and the identification of illness being induced in a child had an impact on the outcomes. Often mis-management of these early stages had resulted in the abuse not being evidenced fully and the child had been put at even greater risk.

Characteristics of the successful management of initial suspicion and identification

The following factors were shown to be necessary in the early stages when abuse was suspected:

- The team were alert to the possibility of illness being induced in children.
- The team members were fully cognisant of its nature and possible consequences.
- The child protection team was part of the multidisciplinary/multi-agency team managing the suspicions and initial identification.
- Suspicions were shared and discussed early on by team members and the management of the identification was a carefully planned piece of work.

Similarly it was found that once it became likely the team was dealing with a case of illness induction syndrome, the way in which the initial assessment was undertaken affected the outcome.

Characteristics of the successful initial assessment and management

The following features were also necessary to bring about a good outcome:

- Objective and irrefutable medical information.
- The information gathered included the team's observations of the child and his or her family's interactions and behaviour.
- All relevant members of the multidisciplinary team were engaged in obtaining comprehensive medical, psychiatric and social histories so that the team had a clear and accurate picture of the family.
- All interventions – in the child and family and in the professional systems – were managed by the inter-professional team.

Characteristics of the long-term assessment and management

The long-term outcomes were found to be related to two key dimensions: the quality of professional interventions; and the context in which this work was undertaken.

The outcomes were poor in systems where:

- irrespective of whether the family was being worked with on a statutory basis or solely in partnership, the focus was not on the need to protect the child;
- the professionals involved with the family had seen their role in a minimalist way, to monitor what was happening with the child and family but not to intervene in a planned and coordinated way to assess the family's capacity to change;
- the interventions by many agencies were uncoordinated and unmanaged;
- either a limited, short-term therapeutic package was offered or no therapeutic help at all.

By contrast, the outcomes were good in systems where:

- the team's focus was on child protection, not simply on the provision of medical or care services;
- all interventions were based on a comprehensive assessment of the child and family and were planned;
- the inter-professional team managed the therapeutic and/or statutory interventions, which may have been undertaken within the context of a child protection plan or an agreement made with the parents;
- a comprehensive therapeutic package was planned and delivered over a sustained period of time.

Conclusion

In summary, the findings showed that there were six features of management that all need to be present to ensure a good outcome for a child in whom illness has been induced.

- The paediatric service is competent and able to distinguish between the organic and abusive aspects of a child's presenting symptoms.
- The hospital staff are organised such that members of the psychosocial team are attached to a particular ward/team.
- The induction of illness in a child is conceived of as an abuse of the child and the management is carried out within a child protection framework.
- The professionals involved with the child and family function using a coordinated multidisciplinary, multi-agency approach.
- All interventions are planned on the basis of a comprehensive assessment of the child and family, which incorporates an understanding of the function of the illness induction for the family.
- Therapeutic work is undertaken over a sustained period of time.

It may be that if all these aspects of management had been present in the cases in this study, the outcomes for many more of these children would have been good.

References

Bools, C N, Neale, B A and Meadow, S R (1992) 'Co-morbidity associated with fabricated illness (Munchausen syndrome by proxy)', *Archives of Disease in Childhood,* 67, 77-79

Bools, C N, Neale B A and Meadow, S R (1993) 'Follow-up of victims of fabricated illness (Munchausen syndrome by proxy)', *Archives of Disease in Childhood,* 69, 625-630

Department of Health (1991) *Working Together Under the Children Act 1989.* HMSO

Eminson, D and Postlethwaite, R (1992) 'Factitious illness: recognition and management', *Archives of Disease in Childhood,* 67, 1510-1516

Gray, J and Bentovim, A (1994) 'Forty-one children with induced illness syndrome: A descriptive and follow-up study', Paper presented at the Royal College of Psychiatrists Meeting, London

Gray, J, Milla, P and Bentovim, A (1993) 'The identification and management of induced illness in children', Paper presented at the British Paediatric Association Conference, Warwick

Griffith, M (1988) 'The family systems of Munchausen syndrome by proxy', *Family Process*, 27, 423-437

Manthei, D, Pierce, R, Rothbaum, R, Manthei, U and Keating, J (1988) 'Munchausen syndrome by proxy: covert child abuse', *Journal of Family Violence*, 3, 2, 131-140

Masterson, J and Wilson, J (1987) 'Factitious illness in children: the social worker's role in the identification and management', *Social Work in Health Care*, 12, 4, 21-30

Meadow, S R (1977) 'Munchausen syndrome by proxy: the hinterland of child abuse', *The Lancet*, 2, 343-345

Meadow, S R (1982) 'Munchausen syndrome by proxy', *Archives of Disease in Childhood*, 57, 92-98

Meadow, S R (1985) 'Management of Munchausen syndrome by proxy', *Archives of Disease in Childhood*, 60, 385-393

Neale, B A, Bools, C N and Meadow, S R (1991) 'Problems in the assessment and management of Munchausen syndrome by proxy abuse', *Children and Society*, 5,4, 324-333

Rees, S (1987) 'Munchausen syndrome by proxy: another form of child abuse', *Practice*, 3, 267-283

Rosenberg, D (1987) 'Web of deceit: a literature review of Munchausen syndrome by proxy', *Journal of Child Abuse and Neglect*, 11, 547-563

Samuels, M, McClaughlin, W, Jacobson, R, Poets, C and Southall, D (1992) 'Fourteen cases of imposed upper airway obstruction', *Archives of Disease in Childhood*, 67, 162-170

Southall, D, Stebbens, V, Rees, S, Lang, M, Warner, J and Shinebourne, E (1987) 'Apnoeic episodes induced by smothering: two cases identified by covert video surveillance', *British Medical Journal*, 294, 1637-1641

Waller, D (1983) 'Obstacles to the treatment of Munchausen by proxy syndrome', *Journal of the American Academy of Child Psychiatry*, 22, 80-85

12. Supervision of convicted perpetrators

Paul Miller, Assistant Chief Probation Officer, Lincolnshire Probation Service

Barbara Miller, Probation Officer, Lincolnshire Probation Service

The organisation and purpose of the probation service

There are 55 probation areas in England and Wales operating autonomously but within a framework of national standards and Home Office guidance. (There is no probation service in Scotland where social work departments have responsibility for tasks carried out by the probation service in England and Wales.) The probation service is funded 80 per cent by the Home Office and 20 per cent by local authorities.

The probation service serves the courts and the public by:

- supervising offenders in the community;
- working with offenders, so that they lead law-abiding lives in a way that minimises risk to the public;
- safeguarding the welfare of children in family proceedings.

The probation service provides courts with advice and information on offenders, mostly in written reports, to assist in sentencing decisions. It supervises offenders made subject to community orders (probation orders, community service orders and combination orders) and in doing so seeks to protect the public and help reduce reoffending. The probation service also assists prisoners before and after release, many of whom will be subject to statutory supervision by a probation officer once released into the community.

In addition to its work with offenders, the probation service provides courts with information regarding the best interests of children in family disputes.

The core skills of a probation officer

In criminal work, a probation officer's main tasks are to prepare reports for court and supervise offenders in the community. Supervising offenders often involves challenging denial (particularly in relation to sex offenders) and in these cases probation officers do not easily accept offenders' explanations for their actions.

In providing information and advice to courts, probation officers are expert sentencing advisers. They are skilled at analysing offending behaviour; for example, the behaviour and motivation resulting in offence(s), patterns of previous offending and problems related to offending. These skills are used in working **with** offenders to confront their behaviour, to identify patterns/triggers and to help to devise strategies for avoiding further offending.

The probation service has a major responsibility to protect the public (this includes the victim) while supervising offenders. Thus risk assessment skills are central to the role of the probation officer. This requires detailed knowledge of the circumstances of the offence and previous offending behaviour to identify trigger factors that are likely to predispose someone to reoffend.

Probation officers are social work trained and have other skills but here we have focused on the unique core skills they will bring to interagency work.

The nature of probation service involvement in MSBP and consequent child protection issues

As has been indicated by the case material in Chapters 2 and 8 by Gretchen Precey and John Fox respectively, the main role of the probation service in relation to Munchausen syndrome by proxy (MSBP) is in the preparation of pre-sentence reports and supervision of offenders on community orders or subject to post-release supervision.

The nature and degree of a probation officer's involvement in child protection issues depends on the proximity of the perpetrator to the victim(s) or potential victim(s). The probation service will certainly be fully involved when there is close and continuing proximity, for example when a conviction leads to a community order and the perpetrator remains a primary carer for the victim. In such circumstances it is highly likely that the work of the probation service will be mediated through interagency child protection systems, as one of the paramount aims of supervision will be the protection of the victim and prevention of further offending. The probation service should then be a key contributor to and have an active presence in child protection meetings.

If the perpetrator is serving a prison sentence where there is no family contact, and where the offender will not be returning to the community in which she or he offended, then contact with other child protection agencies will be considerably less. Nevertheless, the probation service via the 'home' probation officer or the prison probation officer will ensure child protection issues are addressed in the release plan and social services consulted. This involves following the procedure in relation to the release of schedule one offenders as recently laid down by the Home Office. Broadly speaking, a schedule one offender is someone who has been convicted of an offence against a child. Further details should be available in local area child protection committee procedures. Each probation service will also have a procedure for dealing with schedule one offenders in their area.

The length of time for which a probation officer is required to supervise an offender varies depending on the length of the community order or post-release supervision. A probation order can be between six months and three years; a combination order (probation and community service combined) can be between one year and three years; post-release supervision can be between three months and life (for someone released on life licence). Offenders can be breached (returned to court) for failing to keep to the requirements of their community order and, in the case of those subject to post-release supervision, possibly recalled to prison. Probation officers therefore exercise some control over offenders in the community and it is particularly important that other child protection agencies appreciate the probation officer's position. National Standards for the Probation Service 1995 require probation officers to take breach action following two unacceptable failures by offenders to comply with their order.

As mentioned above, in cases of MSBP where the victim is a child, child protection will be of paramount concern. There are occasions when the agreed aims of the case conference or core group can be furthered by a probation officer exercising control over an offender by threatening to take, or taking, breach action. For example, if an offender is not complying with a requirement of a community order to receive medical treatment and it is an aim of the case conference for the treatment to resume, breach action can lead to the offender complying with the requirement. On other occasions, the offender may be openly flouting the requirements of their order (and thereby the expectations of the court) but the probation officer may be under pressure (overtly or otherwise) from the case conference or core group **not** to take breach action.

An example would be where the offender is a primary carer (possibly the only one) and their removal from the family would damage or severely disrupt continuity of care which is viewed as being in the child's best interest.

Breach in child protection cases can present a dilemma for the probation service, which MSBP can make more complex. It seems the probation service's authority over an offender can be a boon or, at times, a burden in interagency child protection work. We would ask other agencies to appreciate the dilemma of breach action.

What the probation service brings to work with MSBP

a. Managing dangerousness in service users

The probation service brings to work with MSBP expertise, experience, skills and procedures derived from its supervision of serious risk/dangerous offenders and sex offenders. All probation areas will have internal procedures to monitor probation officers' supervision of dangerous offenders, sex offenders and child protection cases. In Lincolnshire the procedure begins with the internal registration of relevant cases. Registration is often automatic in the case of schedule one offenders, life sentence prisoners and those who have committed serious offences such as robbery, aggravated burglary or violence. Probation officers can also submit for registration offenders whom they consider dangerous or who they feel present a serious risk to the public.

The supervising officer will undertake a risk assessment, which details patterns of previous offending, identifies and analyses the circumstances of the present offence, assesses the offender's motivation and attitude to the offence, and identifies those circumstances or factors which if they re-occur singly or together are likely to lead to a further offence. Factors could be drink/drugs, breakdown of a significant relationship, resumption of a significant relationship, opportunity, type of employment or money. Monitoring of these factors will be part of the supervision plan and the probation officer will work, hopefully with the offender, to minimise these factors.

The dangerous offender procedure requires registered cases to be reviewed at regular intervals. The reviews are carried out with the supervising probation officer by senior probation officers and can involve assistant chief probation officers. This system holds the supervising officer to account but also protects him or her, as critical decisions about the supervision of dangerous offenders are shared through the organisation. In parole, life sentence and discretionary release cases, review and accountability continues from the local area to the Home Office. Thus there are checks and balances designed to protect the public and minimise risk.

Through its procedures, the probation service questions supervising officers' judgement and interpretation of information. Regular reviews by management help maintain organisational objectivity and prevent supervising officers being drawn into the offender's frame of reference and his or her view of their circumstances. Thus, there is an organisational culture to question, challenge and analyse patterns of behaviour and not accept things at face value.

Our experience is that this culture does not feature to the same degree in other agencies. It is probably not necessary for other agencies (involved in interagency child protection work) to have this culture to achieve their objectives. For example, health service bodies perhaps first and foremost see MSBP sufferers as patients to be helped, believed and treated rather the questioned or doubted. A series of presentations by an individual for medical treatment may be seen as a series of separate treatments rather than a pattern of behaviour. This is a consequence of the fact that health service personnel see a variety of people as patients and patients do not always see the same health service personnel. This is not a criticism, simply an indication that the organisational culture of the health service leads to its personnel not routinely having the same approach to dangerous offenders as the probation service.

Understanding the link between sex offender behaviour and MSBP

The probation service has developed expertise in working with sex offenders, particularly in recent years. The Home Office document entitled *Supervision of Sex Offenders,* published in 1992, records the features of sex offenders that distinguish them from offenders involved in other types of crime. For example, sex offences are rarely isolated, one-off incidents and sexual offending tends to become more entrenched over time with patterns of escalating seriousness. Perhaps the feature that has most influenced the probation service's approach to work with sex offenders is that they are often heavily defended with denial. They justify their behaviour and avoid responsibility. This contributes towards a high rise of reoffending.

These features can, in our view, be applied to MSBP sufferers. Probation officers have to challenge denial vigorously in working with sex offenders and encourage them to take responsibility for their offending and their inevitable power over victims. We find there is usually willingness on the part of other agencies to accept our assessment of the dangerousness a sex offender presents to children. In contrast, we find it is much harder for other agencies to accept our assessment of the dangerousness of a MSBP sufferer who presents as a concerned parent. Yet the probation officer will have applied the same assessment techniques.

It becomes impossible for the probation officer to challenge heavily defended MSBP perpetrators subject to statutory supervision by the probation service if other agencies do not accept the officer's assessment of the perpetrator as an offender. The MSBP perpetrator can easily undermine the officer's focus on offending behaviour and play one agency off against another.

Conclusion

We have sought to illustrate the approach the probation service brings by virtue of its purpose, skills and culture to work with MSBP sufferers and to attendant child protection matters. As MSBP is rare and there is relatively little written material on the subject, workers of any agency may find themselves working with colleagues who doubt the possibility of MSBP in a particular case. There is certainly a training need within the probation service and we therefore welcome Chapter 14 on training issues.

Finally, we would like to highlight practice principles that we have found helpful in our work with MSBP and which in essence are those recommendations for practice contained in *Dangerous Families: assessing and treating child abuse* (Dale and others, 1986).

a) 'Clearing the ring'. By this we mean that the number of professionals working with the family should deliberately be reduced to the minimum necessary to provide the family with a service and to protect the child adequately. It is easy for many professionals to be working with a family without integration or clarity. This brings us onto our next point.

b) Those involved with the family should be clear about their role and responsibility and **should hold to these boundaries.**

c) The interagency system should be able to carry out any actions it says will follow from a perceived increased risk to the child in terms of any legal proceedings. Planning and forethought is therefore crucial, as is the collective will to 'see things through' in order to protect the child.

Reference

Dale and others (1986) *Dangerous Families: assessing and treating child abuse.* Routledge

13. Treatment – from victim to survivor

Norma Howes, Independent Therapist, Practitioner, Trainer and Consultant

How my first MSBP survivor presented herself to me

Julie came to see me just after her release from psychiatric hospital. She was wary and said she was scared to start with a new counsellor. When asked why she thought she wanted to see me, she said a friend at work had suggested she should see me because I worked with people who had been abused as children, not that that had happened to her.

She told me she was 23, had an older sister and that the previous year she had attempted suicide on the anniversary of her brother-in-law's suicide. She said she could not remember why or what had happened after she had taken the pills – she had just woken up in hospital. On discharge she had been referred to the community psychiatric team for support and had been seen by six community psychiatric nurses over the next nine months.

She smiled as she spoke about the number of people she had seen and said that she expected I would not like her nor want to see her for long either. This too was said with a smile which did not fit the flat yet angry, hurt tone she used. There had been several further short spells of in-patient treatment in the past year. She had been discharged home with a diverse amount of medication which she knew all about, including the side effects, dosage recommendations and toxicity.

In answer to my questions about herself and her childhood, she said she had had an idyllic childhood but had no memory of anything particularly happy or sad. She said there was certainly no abuse but, rather oddly, she had a feeling that she wanted to remember her childhood and that she was sure I would be the right person to help her.

She said she had had several admissions to hospital as a child and lost some time from school because she was poorly. She thought she was quite bright and could have done better at school but had not taken up any further education. She had had several short-term jobs and had thought about being a nurse or a nursery nurse.

While she spoke to me it was clear she was dissociating. She would stop talking for some seconds or minutes and appear unaware she had done so. Her behaviour did not match what she was saying: she would smile and say she was angry or smile and say how puzzled or hurt she was by something someone had said or done. She was dismissive of herself, seeing no value in herself as a person and she kept repeating that no doubt I would not like her or that she would do something that would make me stop seeing her.

Over the following months we talked about her and her family. Julie was right that she would say and do things that would make me not like her and want to give up on her. She would arrive late and expect the session still to be of the usual length, looking hurt and bewildered and making me feel that I was being unreasonable and uncaring by not extending our time. Similarly, she would begin talking about something that was of great importance to her minutes before the session was due to end, again looking hurt and bewildered when I insisted that the session should end on time.

She would switch from being very dependent and insisting she needed to phone me every day to saying that therapy was rubbish and a waste of time. She was dismissive and arrogant and quoted chapters from books on therapy and psychiatry she said she had read and clearly I had not.

She seemed determined to work hard on her issues and equally determined to sabotage any progress she made. She wanted me to change the way I worked, just with her, to make her seem more special and yet she continually wanted reassurance that she was no different from anyone else I worked with.

She would say she could not trust anyone, yet would talk about intimate and private parts of her life without difficulty but as if she was talking about someone else. She would say that I was the only person she had ever trusted, then follow this up by denying we were talking about her or her situation. She often said she would find seeing a male therapist easier and more comfortable but hated her male psychiatrist and her father. She would say she felt sorry for me having to see her and then be very abusive and angry with me, dismissing me and my work.

From the knowledge Julie had and the information we were able to gather from her medical history, it became clear the Julie had suffered Munchausen syndrome by proxy (MSBP) abuse at the hands of her mother. Details of how to gather such information are provided later in the chapter.

Julie certainly challenged and tested my 'comfort' and knowledge in working with adult survivors. I have worked with survivors of childhood trauma for many years, survivors of often the most appalling physical, emotional and sexual abuse. Much of what she said and did was similar to that of the other abuse survivors with whom I had worked, but there were also some interesting differences. Every survivor's response to their trauma is unique, although similar patterns and issues are found in the research and literature. Thus their needs and healing pathways are as individual as they are.

Julie was the first of four young women with whom I have now worked who are survivors of MSBP abuse. Only one of the mothers has had a formal diagnosis confirmed. None of the young women had children of her own.

Without the knowledge I had of the issues, the likely short- and long-term effects of their abuse on all trauma survivors, together with the support of much needed supervision, it would have been only too easy to react negatively to the women's anger, despair and the lack of trust.

Issues for therapists working with adult survivors of MSBP abuse

The need for a full history

As full a history as possible should be put together, within the bounds of confidentiality. This may be difficult. Much of the information will come from the victim/survivor. Listen out for:

- unexplained and/or repeated hospital admissions – most children know why they were in hospital either from their own knowledge or family folklore;
- time lost from school;
- many visits to the doctor, sometimes weekly but with no particular reason remembered or recorded;
- unexplained gaps in time sequences;
- inconsistencies in the description of feelings about relationships with the family;
- unexplained and seemingly unaccountable anger or dismissive laughter towards professionals such as teachers and doctors

but conversely knowing them and referring to them by their first names.

Distortions in thinking and perception

Growing up in a very abusive and distorted environment can lead to distortions of thinking and perception. The child begins to wonder whether they feel ill or not, is well or unwell. The child will have had to try make sense of this and will only have been able to apply their own thinking and experience: 'If mum says I am ill then I must be ill. If the doctor is taking what mum says seriously and arranges an admission to hospital with all its attendant dramas and investigations then something must be wrong.' The child cannot allow themselves to think they might be well because if they are well then it is mummy and the doctor and all these other adults who are wrong. The child begins to doubt and loses a sense of trust in themselves and their body responses and thinks 'I must be wrong, there must be something wrong with me. I must be bad to think that mummy is wrong.' To think otherwise either consciously or unconsciously would mean not trusting one of the most important people in their life and all those other adult people on whom the child must depend for all physical and emotional nurturing. An added tension for the child is that positive verbal and non-verbal reinforcement and strokes are received from mother by complying with her view that something is wrong.

Any thinking that leads to questioning what is going on is even more puzzling because the parent is seen as being part of the hospital system, respected by staff and doctors. One of the survivors said:

> 'I could see them [the consultant paediatrician and nurses] talking to my mum. They were listening so carefully to what she said. They were laughing and talking together as if they were friends. They asked her if I wanted a bed pan, not me. They asked her how I was, not me. She looked so happy. Nobody asked me what I thought ...'

The women I worked with were attending hospitals, both as out-patients and in-patients between ten and 20 years ago and their experience may to a degree reflect practice on children's wards then. They were not included in any discussions, evaluations or enquiries. If mum said the child was sick all night, it was accepted.

Presence of unresolved traumas and major life issues

In order for anyone to be able to understand what is happening to them, the brain needs to receive data, make sense of it and store it for use, thus enabling sense to be made of future experiences. A narrative must be added to the emotional and physical sensations and feelings to enable the process to be completed and the aroused state relaxed.

An admission to hospital is a traumatic experience for anyone and even more so for a child. If this has never happened before it is even more terrifying. The caring parent will understand this and explain, using words, drawings and books, just what is happening and give the child a narrative to explain the feelings she or he has. An example of this is when a child falls. The child feels the pain and terror of the fall. The parent explains what has happened and why. The narrative and feelings can be stored for future access. Another fall is understood and does not result in the same level of terror.

We have all smiled at the often funny and strange interpretations children can put on their non-abusive experiences as they search for a narrative themselves. Abuse happens in secret and is often denied. Seldom is a narrative supplied by the parent to enable the child to make any sense of the overwhelming feelings. The child has to depend on his or her own limited repertoire of narratives. Their explanation will not make sense of the range of their feelings and sensations. The memory cannot be processed and stored to enable sense to be made of future events. Each additional trauma adds to the confusion and terror.

In MSBP abuse the mother is not there for her child; indeed she requires the child to meet her own needs. The child's feelings and sensations are denied or distorted. The narrative and the feelings are seldom if ever congruent. The visit to hospital and the subsequent investigations – which would be traumatic in any event – become even more bewildering and terrifying.

Survivors have all spoken of the additional, often unrecognised or underestimated, trauma of having a mother who looks all right, is articulate and is seen by the system as caring and loving but who, in fundamental ways, is emotionally lacking. In addition, her behaviour is very abusive: suffocating, injecting, poisoning, ignoring and requiring the child to deny themselves by putting aside their own needs for feeding, toileting and nurturing to meet the parent's needs in order to receive approval in return.

Gender of perpetrator

From the current research available, most MSBP abuse is perpetrated by females in the caring/mothering role. The research indicates the father is superficially stereotyped as absent or unconcerned and this is confirmed by the comments of the survivors with whom I have worked. The complexity of the parent/child relationship cannot be underestimated. The research done so far indicates that the mother is seen initially as attached, caring and concerned. She is likely to have been encouraged as prime carer and involved in care plans. The child sees her talking with and being respected by other professionals.

One of the expected repercussions of the gender issue for me as a female therapist is in the transference and countertransference of feelings: transference being related to the client's feelings, including her own projections, experienced in relation to the therapist; countertransference referring to the therapist's feelings aroused by contact with the client. However, knowing the theory does not always lead to immediate understanding, coping skills or management of the feelings aroused.

A survivor sees women now, as mum was then, as being untrustworthy but needed. If I behave in a trustworthy way and am trusted as the therapist, then what mum did and did not do means mum was not trustworthy. The emotional pain of that realisation is enormous. The therapy or the therapeutic trust that is being established has to be stopped and is sabotaged in order to avoid feeling angry with her mother's abusive behaviour and perhaps to preserve some relationship with her.

It has been common for me to be blamed by MSBP survivors for being in this work for myself and to meet my own needs. If I am not clear about my own motivation, the countertransference will then impact on me, my work and the therapeutic relationship, by making me doubt myself and my competence. Awareness of the transferences and countertransferences can enable them to be used in a powerfully positive way.

Self-blame

A survivor's sense of self-blame is increased by the child's coping mechanisms: the dissociation and denial of her own physical and emotional feelings which enable the child to collude with, or actively promote ill health, to please the mother and the other professionals. These outside people could be seen by the child as colluding or easily duped and therefore cannot be trusted. However, the child needs to preserve trust, indeed cannot not trust. To enable the trust to be preserved she has to find a way of absolving her mother and the others of blame. This is made bearable by self-blame and the blame and anger that should be outside is brought inside, protecting the mother, preserving the relationship and reinforcing the victim's poor self-esteem and worth.

The sense of self-blame can be reduced in the victim by a label/diagnosis being given to the mother's behaviour so that the mother can be seen as being ill and not having acted with premeditated maliciousness.

All children will look inside themselves for the answer to any relationship problems. Having found self-blame as a solution to the narrative explanation they need, they will hold on to it tenaciously. To believe there is something wrong with the carers/parents is just too psychologically devastating. This feeling that 'there is something wrong with me and all this is my fault' is reinforced by the approval of the parent/perpetrator by the system and the approval of the child by the carers and the system. This is reinforced by doctors using phrases such as, 'We are doing this to try to find out what is wrong with you'. If this could be changed to 'We are trying to find out why you are here' or 'We are trying to find out why your mother brought you here' this would make a great difference, not only to victims of MSBP abuse but to all children, whether or not they are abused, because it begins to supply a narrative solution which is extended to the child.

It is highly likely that there will have been collusion and co-operation by the victim, which resulted in abuse. As a therapist with an adult's knowledge of behaviour and particularly of deviant behaviour, I can understand why this happened. I can therefore excuse the child's behaviour and say the words 'This was not your fault'. The child/adult may intellectually be able to agree but that will not immediately change the emotional belief. To please the therapist, repeating the previous pattern of pleasing other adults, the victim appears to agree but inside will remain puzzled, confused and again be convinced that adults do not know what they are talking about. *Even more likely*, they will blame themselves for not being reassured, thus increasing the sense of self-blame.

Attachment and dependency

All the women I have worked with have had either flawed or non-existent primary attachment with their carer, who was either dangerous or negligent. Their trust had to be invested in people who were untrustworthy but who were viewed by those with whom they come into contact as being caring and trustworthy.

The fact that the perpetrator of the abuse sees the child merely as an object has a profound effect on that child's ability to relate to his or her world and to make and sustain other relationships and friendships. This goes on into adulthood.

The challenge to the therapist: clarity of boundaries and role

The lack of other relationships for the adult/survivor within the extended family or with friends is likely to increase the level of dependency on the therapist. I am seen as a potential mother, father, sibling, lover, enabler. The difficulty in trusting and depending on someone as much as this can lead to testing and over-dependency. I have found that just when the initial trust is thought to have been established, it is sabotaged and challenged. Having worked through that, there is a huge over-dependence and reliance on me, which often results in testing whether I care enough to bend or break boundaries. It is tempting to be seen as caring and kind by offering more. I have felt at times that I was being cruel in not bending or loosening some of the time and other boundaries. Yet when boundaries have been so seriously broken in childhood, one of the best ways I can show how much I care is to hold to the boundaries and rules established early in the therapy. The need for good supervision and/or working as part of a team cannot be overemphasised if this is to be accomplished.

As shown above, many demands are put on the therapist to be all things to the victim. Confusion and chaos are likely to have been the victim's experience of her relationship with her carers. This may well have been reflected in fragmented and uncoordinated service provision during both childhood and adult life. Demands may therefore be put on the therapist to be:

- therapist (with the victim);
- investigator (assisting the police, researching records);
- rescuer (helping and taking care of all the victim's needs);
- expert witness (in care or criminal proceedings);
- teacher (at case conferences and meetings as the person who not only understands but has experience of dealing with MSBP);
- facilitator (helping the victim to articulate his or her needs);
- parent (replacing the lost parent of the victim).

Clarity of role must be maintained despite the often subtle but enormous pressure from the victim, the system and from within. It is flattering and tempting to be offered the opportunity to be all things to all people.

Helping to heal

The time it takes

It takes time to heal from any trauma. Each mind has its own timescale and this needs to be respected. When trust has been so distorted and from such an early age it takes a long time to trust again and to use that trust as the basis for healing. Offering more time will not necessarily help: there will never be enough time. Maintaining the boundaries in role and time will be much more effective in the short-term and long-term. This can be difficult. When someone tells me I am the only person she ever trusted **and** how much she needs me **and** sincerely means it, then asks for ten extra minutes or an extra phone call or an additional session, it feels cruel to say no. Yet the answer must be no, however difficult this may be. The temptation to say yes and the feelings aroused by saying no must be talked through and dealt with in supervision.

Understanding dissociation

An increasing amount of research and therapy is being done in the assessment and treatment of the perpetrators of MSBP, as well as all other forms of abuse. Many perpetrators, when describing what was happening when they hurt the child, describe themselves as being 'dissociated'. Dissociation is a disturbance or alteration in the normally integrated functions of identity, memory or consciousness. It is an easily accessible and extraordinarily useful coping mechanism automatically used by everyone at times of stress or trauma. A sense of being outside watching oneself do something or being on the ceiling is not uncommon. This process of dissociation allows the child to be objectified, the abuse to continue and the abuser to continue to see herself or himself as the loving parent as well as be seen as the loving parent by others.

Children also know that dissociation works for them. Their knowledge of what is happening can be separated from their feelings, their body sensations separated from their behaviour. What starts out as entirely helpful and functional can with prolonged use become unhelpful and dysfunctional. I cannot commend too strongly increased knowledge and understanding of the theories of dissociation and its impact on behaviour, affect, sensation and knowledge for anyone working with survivors of trauma. This can also enable the survivors themselves to understand more clearly the responses and needs they experienced as a child and those they are experiencing in the present.

Dissociation and its potential resultant disorders are highly responsive and treatable if understood and dealt with appropriately. Interested readers are referred to the references at the end of this chapter.

Dealing with self-harm

All the survivors of MSBP abuse with whom I have worked have used various means of self-harm, from alcohol and drug misuse to cutting and swallowing objects. The reasons for this behaviour were as complex and as individual as the women themselves. For one it was to prove she was alive and not an object, not only to herself but to everyone else by showing she had blood. For another, the resulting admission to hospital, her familiar refuge and 'home' fulfilled her needs to be treated with kindness by the staff, repeating old patterns and meeting her needs as both the child victim she was and the adult she now is.

When the purpose of the self-harming behaviour was clear, I learned how necessary it was to be tough in dealing with it. The therapeutic contract with each woman was reviewed to make it clear that self-harming was not allowed and breaking this boundary would be treated as any other boundary violation: in other words, if the contract were broken, the therapy would stop. A great deal of time and support was needed in looking for other ways of coping, but without exception the behaviour stopped.

Supporting survivors to recover their own history

Where possible, the victim/survivor should be enabled and supported to obtain for themselves additional details about their history from medical, school, social services and police records. If the therapist does this for them, it may feel as if someone is again 'doing things to them', thus repeating one of the dynamics of the abuse.

Validating what was real and what was perceived through researching medical and other records has proved valuable and helpful but also very painful. The pain of realising their mother was doing such awful things and that she could deceive paediatricians and other professionals is enormous.

> 'I trusted everyone then. They would all smile at her and think she was great. I really thought there must be something wrong with me. I wondered if I was real and sometimes if I even existed. I thought I was going mad. I still do.'

Another benefit from researching the records is the confirmation of the ages at which the various traumas occurred. This helps a great deal in understanding the impact of the traumas on the child's whole functioning, and in identifying the likely repercussions, issues and consequences for the child then and now. Saying the words 'this was not your fault' too early in the therapeutic process could in fact be more damaging for the survivor. It confirms the thinking that people do not understand and that she or he was right to depend on her or his own inner conviction of self-blame. Dealing with this issue must become an integral and ongoing part of the therapy: simply saying the words will never be enough.

Conclusion

This is an exciting, new and demanding area of work. Good practice and good therapy cannot be over-emphasised. I learned how important it was to do the things I know I do well and what I knew worked with other people. Developing new techniques and new practices with a client with a new 'diagnosis' or label may lead to confusion, exhaustion and distress for both therapist and client. Hearing about new coping mechanisms and survival strategies is challenging. The issues of transference and countertransference need careful analysis and discussion in supervision. Grandiosity and narcissism are highly infectious. Great care is needed in sticking to very firm boundaries. You may well be challenged to listen more, learn more and know yourself more. The challenge will be enormous: in order to meet it, taking care of yourself is not just a good idea but is absolutely essential.

References

Bowlby, J (1988) *A Secure Base: parent/child attachment and healthy human development.* Basic Books

Braun, B (1988) 'The BASK model of dissociation' *Dissociation 1,* 4-23

Briere, J (1992) *Child Abuse Trauma: theory and treatment of lasting effects.* SAGE

Herman, J (1992) *Trauma and Recovery.* Pandora Books

Horwath, J and Kessel, M (1994) 'Munchausen syndrome by proxy: issues faced by social workers', *Professional Social Work,* March 1995

Parnell and Day (1994) *Identification and Treatment of Munchausen syndrome by proxy* Presentation at 5th National Conference on Abuse, Trauma and Dissociation, Tyler USA

Ross, C (1989) *Multiple Personality Disorder: diagnosis, clinical features and treatment.* Wiley Interscience

Stern, D (1985) *The Interpersonal World of the Infant.* Basic Books
Yorker, C Y (1995) 'Munchausen syndrome by proxy as a form of
family violence', *Family Violence and Sexual Abuse, Bulletin,* 10
(3-4), 34-39

14. Issues for training

Jan Horwath, Child Care Training Manager and

Lecturer, University of Sheffield

Brian Lawson, Multi-agency Child Protection Trainer,

Sheffield

Whenever a child dies, or there is concern within an organisation about child protection issues, a common response is to consider training as an immediate, quick and effective solution. This implies that there are accepted standards towards which staff should be working and that the actual standards achieved by staff in particular situations fall short. In these circumstances training is seen as the mechanism for reducing the gap between actual and required standards. Yet this is a reactive response and ignores all the other factors that can influence a shortfall in meeting required standards: for example, limited resources, inadequate supervision or a lack of clarity about roles and responsibilities. In situations when the focus is primarily placed on training, standards may not improve, as Mager and Pipe (1970) state:

> 'Solutions to problems are like keys in locks; they don't work if they don't fit, and if solutions aren't the right ones, the problem doesn't get solved.'

When considering training in relation to MSBP it is important that the training begins with policy makers, raising their awareness and providing them with opportunities to consider the other organisational factors that form part of the 'solution'. This approach should enable staff to develop their skills with MSBP by helping them to integrate their training experience in to a practice context where there are clear guidelines and procedures, and a common understanding of individual roles and responsibilities.

For these reasons we outline in this chapter a training strategy that places considerable emphasis on management training. We also consider the training needs of various front-line practitioners and propose strategies for meeting these needs, on a single agency and multidisciplinary basis. The chapter includes a variety of suggested exercises that can be used or adapted for use in training courses on MSBP.

Who needs training?

As Figure 6 illustrates, there are a large number of different professional and support disciplines which have particular training needs in relation to MSBP. We have attempted to indicate the range of professionals within different agencies who will need to develop more specific knowledge and skills if cases are to be managed appropriately and sensitively, and children adequately protected. This list is not intended to be exhaustive but we feel that it will serve as a useful starting point for those who wish to develop a training strategy for addressing MSBP abuse. Not only are there different practitioners within organisations who need training, but there is also a need to train managers at different levels.

Coordination

In our experience, any training provided on MSBP is likely to be 'demand-led' and to follow on from practitioners requesting training in the aftermath of a suspected case of MSBP. We would argue that requests for training should be registered and that the other reasons behind a failure to meet expected standards should be explored prior to any training response. It is likely that any training response will still be affected by the circumstances within which the failure to achieve acceptable standards occurred: for example, a lack of guidelines may have been the reason for failings in the investigation or assessment process.

A pivotal role for the area child protection committee

Given the diversity of training needs indicated above we would suggest that the local area child protection committee (ACPC) would be the most appropriate forum to formulate, coordinate, deliver and evaluate a training strategy. This task could probably be delegated to the training sub-group.

Set up under *Working Together* (Department of Health, 1991), ACPCs have a responsibility:

(a) to establish, maintain and review local inter-agency guidelines on procedures to be followed in individual cases;

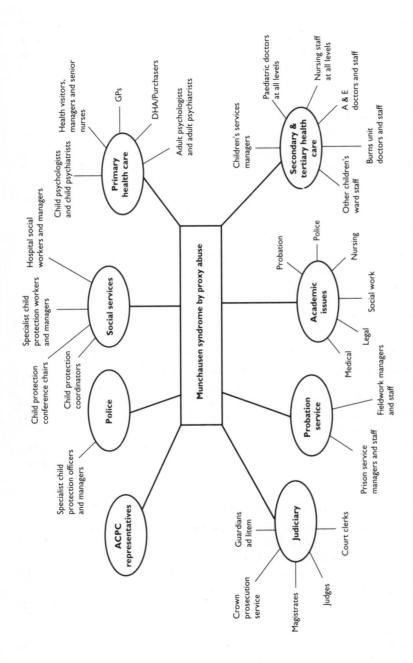

Figure 6   Some of the professionals with training needs in relation to MSBP abuse

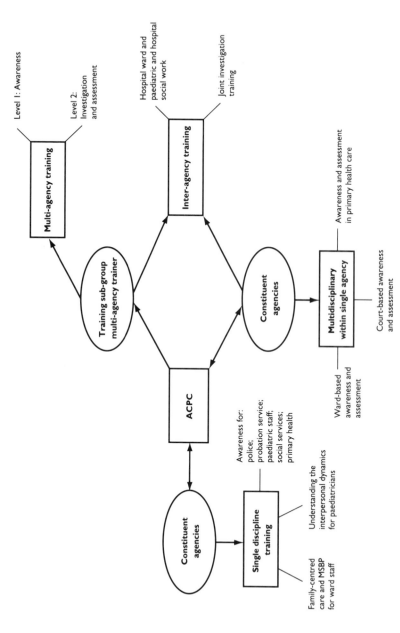

Figure 7   An ACPC-coordinated training strategy and programme in relation to MSBP abuse issues

(b) to monitor the implementation of legal procedures;

(c) to identify significant issues arising from the handling of cases and reports from inquiries;

(d) to scrutinise arrangements to provide treatment, expert advice and inter-agency liaison and make recommendations to the responsible agencies;

(e) to scrutinise progress on work to prevent child abuse and make recommendations to the responsible agencies:

(f) to scrutinise work related to inter-agency training and make recommendations to the responsible agencies;

(g) to conduct reviews required under Part 8 of this Guide;

(h) to publish an annual report about local child protection matters.

(Working Together, para 2.12)

The training strategy

In Figure 7 we have outlined the key elements of a comprehensive training strategy in relation to MSBP. We see a comprehensive training strategy in relation to MSBP comprising five discrete elements:

- incorporation of MSBP issues into foundation training;
- single discipline training within single agencies;
- multidisciplinary training within single agencies;
- inter-agency training between two related agencies;
- multi-agency training.

This presumes that the management training and any policy and procedural changes required are already in place. A suggested process for identifying, developing and implementing a training strategy in relation to MSBP is summarised in Table 9 and described in detail in the following sections.

In the next section we will explore some of the different training events that could be run. Target groups, suggested aims and objectives, proposed content and learning outcomes are detailed in appendicies at the end of the chapter.

Training for managers

Preparatory training for senior managers

In our experience, responses to training on MSBP have been focused on meeting the needs of practitioners. This ignores the Department of Health's view of the role of managers and supervisors:

'Training should help policy makers and practitioners critically evaluate the developing body of knowledge and discuss and implement relevant changes. It should contribute to their knowledge of good policy and practice.' (Department of Health, 1993)

Preparatory training for senior managers should seek to develop common ownership of a training strategy, as the effectiveness of the strategy will be determined by their commitment to subsequent training for front-line managers and practitioners.

Table 9 Summary of a suggested process for identifying, developing and implementing a training strategy for MSBP

At any time:	Incorporation of information regarding MSBP abuse into existing general child protection courses.
Stage 1:	Training for senior managers.
Purpose:	Identify resource policy and procedural issues.
Outcome:	Development of new policy, procedures and services
↓	as necessary.
Stage 2a:	Training for line managers and supervisors (when policy and procedure is developed).
Purpose:	Increase the skills of line managers and supervisors in enabling their staff to respond effectively.
Outcome:	Increased ability of line managers and supervisors to
↓	assist front-line staff.
Stage 2b:	Single discipline awareness training for practitioners (**when policy and procedure is developed**).
Purpose:	Raise awareness of MSBP in more detail and focus specifically on impact roles and responsibilities of individual disciplines.
Outcome:	Increased ability of practitioners to respond
↓	sensitively to suspicions of MSBP abuse.
Stage 3:	Inter-agency training (following awareness training).
Purpose and outcome:	To improve referral, assessment and investigation of suspicions of MSBP abuse.
Stage 4:	Multi-agency training (**following awareness training and inter-agency training**).
Purpose and outcome:	To improve practice response to suspicions of MSBP abuse throughout the child protection system.

Such preparatory training should offer senior managers an opportunity to consider the issues in terms of implications for policy development and practice guidelines. A seminar or development day organised on a multidisciplinary basis, involving an expert, is a productive way of engaging middle and senior managers. The programme could focus on raising their awareness of the issues surrounding MSBP and assessment, and then consider the implications for each agency as well as for inter-agency practice. The training may raise awareness of some current practice weaknesses: for example, inter-agency working or lack of guidelines around the investigative process. The seminar should end with an action plan and a commitment to 'implement relevant policy changes' (Department of Health, 1993). Such training should result in the development of an agreed framework of policy, procedure and practice within which training can be delivered. Ownership of this issue by the local area child protection committee at executive level is of course vital and we explore their role later in the chapter.

An example of a possible programme is to be found in Appendix 1 at the end of this chapter.

Training for front-line managers and supervisors

Once preparatory training for senior managers has taken place and any necessary policy changes have been made, front-line managers supervising practitioners will need training around the supervisory task, as described in Chapter 5. This staff group require an understanding of the complexity of making an assessment in relation to MSBP; knowledge of the way perceptions of staff can become distorted because of their interaction with the perpetrator; and awareness of the role of the supervisor in ensuring assessments remain objective. Supervisors will also require an understanding of the investigative process, guidelines and practice implications.

This framework will enable practitioners to receive appropriate training within a context of clear guidelines and procedures. Supervision will also provide them with the opportunities to translate into practice the skills acquired on the course. The supervisory training may be most appropriately delivered in house, focusing on individual supervision policies. However, more detailed training on CVS guidelines is more appropriately delivered on an inter-agency basis to facilitate joint working. An example of a possible programme is given in Appendix 2.

Training for practitioners

Practitioners' training needs in relation to MSBP

Throughout this book, authors have emphasised the need for a multidisciplinary approach to making an assessment in a suspected case of MSBP. Multi-agency training would enable practitioners to gain greater understanding of each other's roles and responsibilities and ways in which they should work together. Training may also be required within single agencies for particular groups of staff: for example, guidance and training for nursing staff in relation to delivering family-centred care when MSBP is suspected. Also important is training for paediatricians in the seductive interpersonal dynamics they will be required to manage in cases of MSBP abuse.

Different disciplines within a single agency may also require training . For example, primary health care teams should consider ways in which they make an initial assessment and work together to collate evidence in suspected cases of MSBP. It may also be that there is a need for inter-agency training between two different agencies, for example, paediatric doctors, ward staff and the hospital-based social work team looking at how best to handle suspected cases. Some of these needs can be met by incorporating material into existing training programmes and some will require the development of new programmes.

Incorporation of MSBP issues into foundation training

Awareness raising of the issues concerning MSBP abuse can be incorporated into basic child protection training courses for staff who come into contact with children and families in two main areas: as an aspect of physical abuse and as a form of abuse requiring special attention in relation to partnership work with families. *Working Together*, para 6.40, describes MSBP as a form of physical abuse and the Department of Health guide on *Partnership in Child Protection* (Department of Health, 1995a) identifies suspicion of MSBP as one of the limits to partnership (para 5.13).

Foundation training can incorporate information about MSBP when looking at physical injury, including a brief description of MSBP abuse, possible signs and symptoms and an outline of some of the possible difficulties. It can also seek to dispel some of the myths. Stephenson's overview of MSBP in this book may provide useful information (Chapter 1). Issues of MSBP can be introduced when looking at balancing partnership with families with the paramount welfare of the child. Suggested programme outlines are offered in Appendices 3, 4, 5 and 6.

Such a training strategy will also require the development of training materials. In the next section we suggest some training exercises as resources for those involved in training to integrate, modify and adapt according to local need.

Suggested topic areas for training and possible exercises

Throughout this book certain key points have been made about the management of cases of MSBP. Training should attempt to enable participants to gain some common understanding of these key areas:

- The notion of motherhood and its impact on risk assessment
- Parents' v children's rights
- A case of organic disorder or child protection?
- Working together in potential cases of MSBP
- Working with other professionals.

The following are suggestions for exercises that could be used as ways of exploring some of these key areas on training courses. The effectiveness of the exercises will depend on a number of factors: the experience and confidence of the trainers; the size of the group; and the context in which they are delivered. All these exercises need careful consideration as to their appropriate use on a training course. It is beyond the remit of this chapter to explore this in depth, but the reader may find *Good Enough Training* (Hollows, Armstrong and Stainton-Rogers, 1989) a useful guide.

Using the exercises

Any training on a topic as emotive as MSBP is likely to provoke in participants a wide range of responses, from anger to discomfort. Participants may also have flashbacks of their own negative experiences of their mother which can be distressing.

Trainers working in this arena must be prepared to address these situations as they arise. However, there are certain approaches to the training which can be used to try and create a safe environment for learning.

1. Prepare course participants: send them a programme with aims, objectives and learning outcomes. Provide them in advance with an outline of the course content and the styles of

delivery, for example case studies, small group discussion. In this way participants have some idea of what to expect.

2. Co-train: this means that the needs of individual course participants are more likely to be perceived and group process issues more successfully managed.

3. Create a safe environment at the start of the training. Inform participants about the facilities – for example, lunch, toilet. Allow time for introductions and for participants to feel comfortable and ready to learn.

4. Make a group contract or agreement, outlining your responsibilities as trainers and theirs as participants. Consider issues of confidentiality and its limitations. For example, if as a trainer you become aware that a child may be at risk as a result of a course member's practice, then this cannot remain confidential.

5. Plan the programme to begin with relatively 'safe' material. Use the most difficult and distressing in the middle of the course. The case study (see Exercise 4), for example, is 'middle' material.

6. Always complete the day with a debriefing session enabling participants to acknowledge anything they found difficult or negative during the day. It is helpful to finish by getting them to consider positive learning outcomes.

The exercises

Exercise 1: The notion of motherhood

Aims: To gain awareness of the cultural understanding of the term 'motherhood' and its significance to course participants.
To begin to consider how the interpretation of this image impacts on risk assessment.

Running the exercise: The group is asked to bring, or the trainer brings to the course, pictures from magazines, poems etc that convey positive perceptions of a mother.

5 mins The trainer introduces the exercise explaining that research on MSBP perpetrators indicates they are predominantly mothers and our assessments are very much linked with our own images of mothers. (This book can be used as a source of reference.)

20 mins   In small groups participants share their images and discuss common perceptions of 'positive mothering'.

20 mins   The trainer brings the group back together and asks them to share their perceptions. The trainer records these on a flipchart and facilitates a group discussion on common images.

10 mins   The trainer can then give some input on the way mothers, who may be manifesting MSBP behavioural patterns, can present. (See Chapter 1.)

20 mins   The group are asked to comment and consider how many of these behaviours superficially describe a 'positive mother'.

20 mins   The group divide into three sub-groups and consider the implications for making an assessment of possible MSBP from one of the following perspectives:
- issues for professionals;
- issues for mothers;
- issues for child.

15 mins   Each group presents back from their perspective.

The session finishes with discussion around the tensions and subjectivity that can develop, with input from the trainer on professional dangerousness, referring to Chapter 5 in this book.

This exercise leads effectively into the second key area.

Exercise 2: Parents' v children's rights

Aim: To enable participants to consider the implications of a MSBP diagnosis from the perspective of parents and children.

The exercise: A number of different approaches can be used:

Variation 1   The trainer divides the group into two: one to prepare the arguments against the MSBP label from the parents' perspective. The trainer could prepare a handout, based on Chapter 3, that this group could use for reference.

The other half of the group should prepare a case for children's rights arguing for the MSBP label. This group could have a handout prepared by the trainer, based on Chapter 8, highlighting issues for children arising out of the cases John Fox references.

Variation 2 The case study included in this chapter (see Exercise 4) could be used as the basis of a debate to explore issues around parental and children's rights. Some members of the group could argue the case from the perspective of Sarah and evidence available (not including the final incident – Stage 7). Other members could consider the evidence from Tony's perspective.

Variation 3 Alternatively a debate could focus on child protection issues against the need to eliminate organic causes: the paediatrician's dilemma. It may be useful to use Meadow's work (which is referenced in other chapters) and to Chapter 3.

Running the exercise:

30 mins The trainer gives each group time to prepare their case and states that each side will have ten minutes to present their side of the debate. They may choose how to do this, for example one or two spokespersons being fed information by the rest of the group, or each group member making a point.

Approximately 20 mins After the arguments have been presented, the groups can debate with each other. This needs to be time-limited.

At the end of the session the trainer asks the group to 'vote'. For example, if variation one or two is used for debate the vote could be on whether MSBP is a useful label.

This exercise works most effectively with a maximum of 16 course participants.

Exercise 3: When is it child protection?

Aim: To enable course participants to consider the implications for assessment of MSBP behavioural patterns.

Running the exercise: The trainer prepares a number of cards which describe behaviours or experiences of MSBP assessments found in this book, for example 'mother is over anxious'; 'child is brought to hospital by mother who claims child had fits'.

Approximately 20 statements will need to be prepared.

20 mins The trainer divides the group into sub-groups and asks them to consider each of the statements and place them into one of three categories:

1. No cause for concern in terms of child protection.
2. A child protection issue.
3. The ones they debated, discussed and could not agree on.

The trainer asks the sub-group to bring back to the main group statements that come into the third category.

20 mins The trainer facilitates discussion: are there common statements people could not agree on?

10 mins What may be responsible for the diversity of views and opinions?

This technique is adapted from the work of Brown and Baily (1988).

Exercise 4: Working together in potential cases of MSBP

Aims: To enable course participants to raise their awareness of the importance of working together in potential cases of MSBP.

To gain understanding of the role of child protection procedures in potential cases of MSBP.

Exercise: **Case study**

Stage 1 Sarah and her child Tony, aged eight months, present to their general practitioner at the surgery. Tony has seen the doctor on ten previous occasions. On this visit Sarah states that the child is not eating well. The general practitioner examines Tony and notes he is on the 25th percentile, where he has been since birth. The general practitioner assures

Sarah that her baby is making good progress
and there is nothing to worry about. The
general practitioner notes indicate that Tony
has been seen on a number of occasions for
such things as intolerance of his mother's
breast milk and problems in making the
transition from liquid feeds to solids.

Stage 2 The health visitor visits the following week to
undertake a nine-month assessment of Tony.
She notes weight loss and feels Tony is pale
and listless. Sarah presents as very
concerned and is distressed by the continuing
feeding problems.

Stage 3 Two days later, the health visitor is informed
by the paediatric liaison health visitor that
Tony has been admitted to hospital with
acute diarrhoea and vomiting. Tony was
dehydrated but is responding well to medical
treatment.

Stage 4 Tony is discharged home the following day.
The health visitor visits the next day. Sarah
reports more diarrhoea and vomiting. She is
very upset and weepy and bewildered that
Tony was discharged. The health visitor
assesses Tony as looking well and being more
alert than on her previous visit.

That evening Sarah brings Tony to the
general practitioner's surgery and requests
Tony is assessed for food allergies as
diarrhoea and vomiting are continuing –
Sarah is very distressed, and tells the general
practitioner she is concerned her baby will
die. The general practitioner examines Tony
and can find no cause for concern.
That night Sarah presents at casualty in a
very anxious state with Tony semi-conscious.
He is dehydrated, placed on a drip and put in
a single side ward with a bed for Sarah. The
nursing assessment on admission indicates
that Sarah seems competent and caring; she
seems relieved that Tony is now in hospital
and has calmed down. She is taking primary
responsibility for Tony's care.

In the early hours of the morning, Sarah is hysterical. She comes running from the side ward saying Tony has had a fit. Tony appears pale and listless. The senior house officer examines him and decides to do more tests the following day.

Stage 5   The next morning Sarah stops the social worker on the ward and asks for help in getting some medical treatment for Tony. The social worker discusses the situation with the consultant who says they are doing tests and it may be that Tony has a milk intolerance. The social worker reassures Sarah.

Later that afternoon Sarah comes out screaming from Tony's room shouting that Tony has collapsed and is not breathing. The house officer is on the ward and rushes in, to find Tony looking very pale and whimpering.

Stage 6   At the ward round the following day, the social worker raises the possibility of MSBP as all the tests have come back negative. A decision is made to hold a case discussion.

Stage 7   That night one of the staff nurses enters Tony's room to find Sarah with her hand over Tony's nose and mouth. Tony seems to be struggling. The staff nurse shouts and pulls Sarah away. Sarah says she was cuddling Tony and that the nurse was mistaken, but the nurse remains adamant that Sarah was trying to suffocate Tony.

Case discussion or initial case conference

This case study can be used in a variety of ways: each 'stage' can be separated so that the trainer can divide up the case study as they wish and ask the group to make assessments or decisions. For example, the group could be asked to consider what the health visitor should find out from Sarah at the nine-month check or whether the GP could have handled the surgery visits from Sarah and Tony differently. Similarly, this structure can be used to bring in information that is more locally relevant.

Background information is provided for a case discussion, **to be held before the final incident** (Stage 7) described above. The purpose of focusing on the case discussion is to give the group an opportunity to explore issues around assessment in possible cases of MSBP, when there is no clear evidence available.

It is also possible to adapt the information to use for an initial case conference after the incident described in Stage 7.

Whichever way it is used, the trainer should ensure appropriate information is made available according to local guidelines and procedures. For example, would family members be invited to a case discussion? Would the social worker have spoken to Colin? Would the GP share information on Sarah's medical history?

Background information for the case discussion

N.B. This should be used in conjunction with the information available to each professional in the case study.

Consultant – You have not ruled out MSBP but are concerned that all organic causes are considered. You are anxious that you do not miss an organic problem, as you feel that this could still be a possibility.

Ward sister – You have developed a good relationship with Sarah. Your assessment is that she is a caring but over-anxious mother.

Night staff report – They register some concerns, feeling Sarah is up with Tony more than most other mothers. One of the student nurses thinks she saw Sarah giving Tony a drink which was not recorded.

Social worker – You managed to speak to Colin, Sarah's partner and Tony's father. He is separated from Sarah but came to see Tony on the ward. Colin told you that he only recently separated from Sarah as he felt marginalised during her pregnancy and following the birth of Tony, which led to much discord between the two of them. All Sarah's attention focused on Tony and Colin felt she did not want him doing anything for the baby. Colin feels that Sarah is over-anxious and protective towards the baby, as she lost a child at eight weeks old from a cot death when she was 17 years old. Colin also described Sarah as 'a bit of a hypochondriac' who imagines she has all sorts of acute illnesses.

You feel Sarah presents as an over-anxious mother but wonder about her relationship with Tony as she rarely seems to try and communicate with him and seems very mechanical in the way she handles him. You also have some reservations about your assessment, feeling that you are perhaps looking for things to indicate MSBP and are unsure how this approach fits in with working in partnership with parents.

Health visitor – You did not know what to make of the situation. You are bewildered by the distress and anxiety displayed by Sarah but cannot understand why she expresses no emotion around the pain and suffering Tony must be experiencing.

General practitioner – You have known Sarah since she was 13 when her family moved into the area. You were surprised to discover how thick her own file was, when you came to get Tony's medical notes out for the case discussion.

Sarah's medical history – Since early adolescence, Sarah has been a regular attender at the general practitioner's surgery. She had regular referrals to various hospital consultants for various ailments, that seemed to have no organic causes. The general practitioner's notes indicate that she had trouble-free pregnancies and since the birth of Tony has not visited the general practitioner in her own right. Sarah gave birth to a baby girl when she was 17 and living at home. The baby died in her sleep aged eight weeks, from Sudden Infant Death Syndrome.

Tony – No problems during pregnancy or delivery, but he is small, having been on 25th percentile since birth. Inquiries at the casualty department at the hospital and in the next town, indicated Tony had been taken to hospital on five previous occasions, with various symptoms described by Sarah. He has never shown any of these symptoms when seen by medical staff on examination.

Sarah's mother (Gill) – Has been very concerned about Sarah and Tony and rang the local social services department for advice two months ago, as she felt that Sarah was making out Tony was ill as a cry for help. She had been told to tell Sarah to make an appointment if it would be of use. Sarah's mother felt there were similarities between the way Sarah fussed over Tony and her previous child Lucy. For example, she insisted on sharing a room with Lucy in case something happened to her in the night. Gill described Sarah as being 'neurotic' about her health always complaining of aches and pains and describing her symptoms to anyone who would listen.

Alternative ways of using the case study

The case study can also be presented in its entirety.

1. Group members can read the case and decide what are the possible indicators of a potential case of MSBP.
2. Participants could consider the roles and responsibilities of those involved, for example the dilemma faced by medical staff of continuing medical tests on Tony; the role of nursing staff in observing the interaction between Sarah and Tony.

3. The trainer could also introduce *Working Together Under the Children Act 1989* and ask the group to consider practice implications, for example when should the police become involved?

The case discussion is designed to highlight some of the issues that can arise when working with suspected cases of MSBP. The following can be highlighted as areas for further discussion, or for course participants to consider in terms of good practice.

1. The power dynamics within the group of professionals: what impact does this have on decision making?
2. How can you work in partnership with a carer if you suspect that they may be abusing their child?
3. What factors determine the weight that is given to information? For example, how much attention was paid to the night staff's observations?
4. Should the GP share information from Sarah's file? (Trainer should refer to the Department of Health guidance on Child Protection and Medical Responsibility, Department of Health, 1995b)
5. Should the police have been involved in this case discussion? Should any other professionals have been invited to the case discussion?
6. Should child protection checks have been completed at this stage?

Exercise 5: Working with other professionals

Aim: To enable course participants to gain some understanding of their own role and that of other professionals in possible cases of MSBP.

N.B. This exercise should be carried out after participants have considered the case study.

Exercise: In single agency groups, participants are asked by the trainer to consider their role and when they would want to involve other professionals.

The trainer asks groups to compare and contrast, highlighting and discussing areas of discrepancies.

Conclusion

Throughout this book professionals have written about their struggles to make assessments in this area of child abuse. We are sure they would all agree with the following:

'If from a list of behaviours, ticks could be put against those which are abusive and crosses against those which are not, the task of practitioners and researchers would be easier.' (Department of Health, 1995c)

Training cannot help practitioners to develop skills that will enable them to make an assessment in terms of ticks and crosses. However, it can ensure that all those working with potential cases of MSBP have an opportunity to explore the values and judgements they may hold that may result in them putting a definite cross, when there is not that certainty. It can enhance the knowledge basis and begin to develop skills in practitioners, enabling them to consider the fact that certain behaviours could potentially have ticks against them in particular situations.

MSBP is a small area of practice. As we have already argued, it forces practitioners and managers to face and to manage some of the most complex and important dilemmas in child protection work. In our experience, receiving effective training in the most difficult and challenging areas of practice leads to an improvement in other areas of practice. Consequently training in MSBP may be a good investment in terms of the likely returns in other areas of practice.

We hope we have also highlighted that training alone is not sufficient. Opportunities must be available for staff to put their training into practice with informed support and within a framework of clear guidelines and procedures.

References

Brown, H and Baily, P (1988) *So you think you know what is normal?* Pavilion Publishing

Department of Health (1991) *Working Together Under the Children Act 1989: a guide to arrangements for inter-agency cooperation for the protection of children from abuse.* HMSO

Department of Health, (1993) *Working with Child Sexual Abuse: Guidelines for trainers and managers in Social Services Departments.* HMSO

Department of Health (1995a) *The Challenge of Partnership in Child Protection: a practice guide.* HMSO

Department of Health (1995b) *Child Protection: Medical Responsibilities.* HMSO

Department of Health (1995c) *Child Protection: Messages from Research Studies in Child Protection.* HMSO

Hollows, A, Armstrong, H and Stainton-Rogers, W (1989) *Good Enough Training: managing and developing training in child sexual abuse – trainers' pack.* National Children's Bureau

Mager and Pipe *in* Buckley, R and Caple, J (1995) *The Theory and Practice of Training.* Kogan Page

Appendix 1

Suggested training/development for senior managers

Assumptions: There has been a case of MSBP in the local area and the issue has raised concern about practice.

Target group: Senior managers with responsibility for finance, policy or procedure within the main statutory and voluntary agencies working with children and families: community health services, acute health services, social services, police, probation, education, NSPCC, guardian ad litem service. Could be delivered to single agency or multi-agency group.

Maximum number: 30

Length of course: 1 day minimum. A further number of sessions may be planned as the strategy develops.

Aims and objectives: 1. For participants to be made aware of the nature of MSBP abuse and its implications for resources, policy, procedure and investigative practice including the appropriate use of CVS.
2. For participants to agree a priority strategy for responding to MSBP, which may include training, and to plan a timetable, structure and process within which it might be implemented.
3. For participants to agree how such a strategy would be evaluated for effectiveness.

Style of delivery: Input from main speaker, question and answer session, small group discussion, small group action planning, handouts.

Trainers required: Guest speaker familiar with and experienced in managing MSBP abuse; two trainers to facilitate group process.

Learning outcomes: By the end of the day participants should:
1. Know what MSBP is and how it should be responded to;
2. Know what the implications of MSBP abuse are in terms of resource policy, procedure and practice for the agency/for the ACPC;
3. Have in place an action plan for a priority strategy with an agreed timetable, structure and process;
4. Have available or have identified information necessary to complete the task successfully.

Appendix 2

Suggested training course for front-line managers/supervisors

Assumption: Training strategy has identified need to improve supervision of practitioners and to monitor progress.

Target groups: Social work front-line managers, detective sergeants/detective inspectors, domestic violence and child protection units, front-line managers probation service, nurse advisers in child protection, designated doctors (child protection), line managers NSPCC, line manager guardian ad litem service. Could be some multi-agency/inter-agency training but would also need single discipline/single agency training.

Maximum number: 16 – 20

Length of course: 2 days

Aims and objectives:
1. For participants to be made aware of the nature of MSBP abuse and its implications for resources, policy, procedure and practice, including investigative practice and the appropriate use of CVS.

2. For front-line managers/supervisors to be aware of the likely impact of the dynamics of MSBP abuse on:
   the worker;
   the manager;
   the supervisory relationship;
   the team;
   the professional network;
   the child.

3. For participants to be able to manage and supervise their staff to undertake such work sensitively with families.

4. For participants to understand how and why CVS may be used and how to manage the process on behalf of staff involved.

5. For participants to be aware of the nature of the assessments that need to be undertaken and why.

6. For participants to have the opportunity to rehearse skills and strategies required to ensure the protection of the child.

Styles of delivery: Input, questions and answers, small group discussions, case study, skill development exercise, action planning, handouts.

Trainers required:	Guest speaker/trainers with experience of MSBP. Senior manager(s) from the appropriate organisation(s) to explain the agreed procedures. Two trainers to facilitate group process and learning.
Learning outcomes:	By the end of the course participants should:

1. Know what MSBP is and how it should be responded to;
2. Know what the implications of MSBP abuse are in terms of resource policy, procedure and practice for the agency/for the ACPC;
3. Know how allegations of MSBP abuse will impact on those involved with the family, themselves and their colleagues;
4. Know how to engage with families sensitively while protecting the child;
5. Know how to manage the process of assessing and implementing CVS where necessary;
6. Have rehearsed and developed some skills in responding and managing the impacts outlined above;
7. Have considered issues of self-care and personal needs for supervision and support.

Appendix 3

Single discipline training within a single agency

Definition and target group:	Training delivered to one discipline only e.g. police officers, social workers, health visitors, paediatricians, probation officers, paediatric nurses, guardians ad litem, psychiatrists.
Maximum number:	24
Length of course:	1 or 2 days
Aims and objectives:	1. To promote a basic awareness among a particular practitioner group of MSBP abuse. (This basic awareness would be the same for different disciplines.)
	2. To promote a particular understanding of how MSBP abuse issues would affect that particular group of practitioners.
	3. To provide the practitioner group with an experience of how a case might unfold and how other people might react. (Material from the case study, see Exercise 4 in this chapter, might be used here, adapted for local needs.)
	4. For participants to understand their responsibility in relation to MSBP abuse and how to discharge that responsibility appropriately in seeking to ensure the protection of the child.
Style of delivery:	Formal inputs, handouts, small group exercises and discussions, case study, skill rehearsal.
Trainers required:	Preferably two trainers who are used to working together and are familiar with the material.
Learning objectives:	By the end of the course participants should:
	1. Know what MSBP is and how it should be responded to;
	2. Know what their role and their responsibilities are in relation to managing allegations of MSBP abuse;
	3. Be aware of how cases of suspected MSBP are likely to progress;
	4. Know how to deal with the difficult and complex dynamics that will have to be addressed;
	5. Know what their responsibilities are in relation to the protection of the child and in dealing sensitivity with children.

Particular practitioners could also pursue specific issues. For example:

For paediatricians: How to deal with the interpersonal dynamics of working with a parent suspected of MSBP.

For probation officers: How to prepare a pre-sentence report and supervise a convicted perpetrator.

For police officers: How to investigate allegations of MSBP appropriately, including the use of CVS.

For paediatric nursing staff: How to maintain principles of family-centred care while working with a suspected case of MSBP.

For social workers: How to undertake investigative and assessment work. How to involve family members appropriately.

Appendix 4

Multidisciplinary training within a single agency

Definition and possible target groups:	This is training which is delivered to a number of different disciplines working within the same agency. Ideally these courses should follow single discipline awareness training. Three main worksites would seem likely to have multidisciplinary training needs around MSBP abuse: primary health care, children's hospital wards and court settings.
Maximum number:	Dependent on worksite and staff release issues.
Length of course:	Could be done on a half-day or full-day basis with further sessions if necessary.
General aims and objectives:	1. To develop a common understanding of and a coordinated response to suspicions of MSBP abuse.
	2. To agree a system for managing the difficult and complex interpersonal dynamics likely to arise out of dealing with a suspected case of MSBP abuse.
	3. To discuss and agree how best to carry out assessment and investigation work in relation to MSBP.
Style of delivery:	Team building focusing on group process, case studies, skill rehearsal and development.
Trainers required:	Trainer with experience in team building, experience of work setting and who is familiar with both group process issues and MSBP.
Learning objectives:	By the end of the training members of the group should:
	1. Have a common understanding of MSBP and the issues involved for the particular worksite;
	2. Have agreed a coherent and consistent multidisciplinary approach to dealing with suspicions of MSBP abuse;
	3. Have agreed a system for managing the conflicts and disagreements that are likely to arise;
	4. Have agreed how to carry out investigation and assessment in relation to suspicions/allegations of MSBP.
Suggested content and emphasis for each worksite:	Primary health care teams should receive training in recognition, referral and management. Here it will be the relationship between GP and health visitor that will be

crucial. However, the importance of checking concerns and getting information from other members of the team should be emphasised.

Hospital ward staff face similar but much more intense issues, as the family may be on the wards regularly and for long periods. Such training should involve paediatric doctors, nurses and ancillary staff, including receptionists and other administrative workers involved in contact with families.

The courts have to make judgements with regard both to the care of children and the guilt or innocence of alleged perpetrators in relation to the criminal aspects of MSBP. Both civil and criminal courts need to be aware of relevant case law and the appropriate use of expert witnesses. This can probably be best achieved through joint training for clerks, magistrates and judges.

Appendix 5

Inter-agency training

Definition:	Inter-agency training usually takes place between two agencies, either working on the same site or sharing a similar responsibility. The most common form of inter-agency training is joint investigation training between the police and social services. Such training should ideally be provided following basic awareness training.
Target group:	Joint training between hospital social workers, police officers and paediatricians in any combination. They may share either a worksite or a common investigative purpose. The group may cross more than one ACPC area, as police forces and hospitals often work with more than one ACPC area.
Number:	Variable depending on area.
Aims and objectives:	For participants to: 1. Improve the quality of investigations into MSBP; 2. Familiarise themselves with any agreed protocol on investigations in relation to MSBP, including the use of CVS; 3. Have an opportunity to operationalise the protocol through the use of a case study; 4. Discuss, agree and implement any practice recommendations arising from the training.
Style of delivery:	Formal input, case study, small group discussion, skill rehearsal and development.
Trainers required:	Senior member of ACPC to explain protocol. Two trainers experienced in MSBP and in the use of CVS. Could be run on a regional or consortia basis.
Learning outcomes:	At the end of the course participants should: 1. Know how to improve investigations into MSBP; 2. Know what investigative and assessment techniques to use and when; 3. Know when it is appropriate to use CVS; 4. Have the necessary skills to implement such a surveillance; 5. Identify areas for improving practice and act on them.

Appendix 6

Multi-agency training

Definition: Training delivered to staff from a number of different agencies and disciplines based at different worksites. Training can be at the same level in organisations (for example practitioners, supervisors, policy makers) or across levels. Such training would ideally be delivered following awareness, multidisciplinary and inter-agency training.

Target group: Any combination of groups already mentioned where a need has been identified in bringing those particular groups together.

Maximum number: 24

Length of course: 1 day

Aims and objectives: To bring participants together to focus on how to work with MSBP abuse effectively through the following processes:
referral
investigation
conference
assessment
core group
court processes.

Style of delivery: Case studies, small group exercises and discussions, action planning, handouts.

Trainers required: Two, who are familiar with both MSBP and multi-agency working.

Learning outcomes: By the end of the course participants should:
1. Be familiar with how cases of MSBP are processed through the child protection and related legal systems;
2. Be familiar with some of the pitfalls along the way and how some of these can be addressed;
3. Be clear about how they can work together effectively to maximise the protection of children while having due regard for the rights and sensitivities of parents.

Conclusion: affirming, challenging, linking and developing practice

Jan Horwath, Child Care Training Manager and Lecturer, University of Sheffield

Brian Lawson, Multi-agency Child Protection Trainer, Sheffield

What, then, are the main messages from this book? What needs to be changed and developed? What further work needs to be done?

We have identified seven areas to draw together and which point the way ahead:

- Re-affirming good principles of practice in child protection
- Re-asserting old recommendations from inquiry reports
- Challenging current practice
- Linking practice developments
- Developing practice
- Restoring trust
- Further exploration

Re-affirming good principles of practice

Sandra Shaw's chapter powerfully illustrates that child protection is best practised within a context of inter-agency work and collaboration. As Hallett (1995) has noted, the United Kingdom leads the world in its development of processes of inter-agency coordination at a management and practice level.

The Cleveland inquiry (1987) established that a key purpose behind inter-agency collaboration was to coordinate and bring together significant information on children and families held by a variety of organisations. This, it was envisaged, would provide for the protection of children without undue intervention into family life. This 'jigsaw approach' is now established practice in relation to inter-agency child protection work.

Nowhere in the child protection field are skilled assessments and information gathering more important than in suspected cases of MSBP. The practice base will be low, given the numbers involved, but the consequences for the child and the family are potentially lethal. Such careful assessments can only be done on the basis of reliable information gathered from as many sources as possible and from as far back as possible. This has been a consistent theme throughout the book, but as the principle is so important to the outcome we are emphasising it again in the conclusion.

There is a growing recognition that organisations have a responsibility for developing and implementing policies on staff care for those employees involved in traumatic work, which includes child protection. In the compilation of this book we have been struck by the often unacknowledged trauma experienced by practitioners working with this form of abuse. MSBP abuse challenges myths and assumptions that are at the core of our ability to function as professionals. In doing so it means practitioners must engage directly with powerful themes of trust, betrayal, belief and denial. This is vividly described by one practitioner who said:

'My experience of MSBP was a nightmare, a world where nothing could be taken for granted, almost an Alice in Wonderland situation, with all these bizarre events that came so near to tragedy. The sense of anger and frustration that so many professional and competent people tried to do their best within a system and way of working that should ensure good practice. Yet there we all were, almost hypnotised and unaware as if a snake were weaving in front of you and you can not take your eyes off it.'

In order to manage the traumatic impact on individuals, organisations need to have in place good supervision, staff care and counselling support systems. Where these services have been in place and taken advantage of, they have been invaluable. Sadly, too, we have been in contact with practitioners for whom the personal cost of child-centred work in this area has been high. This has included at least one practitioner being diagnosed and treated for Post Traumatic Stress Disorder, as a result of prolonged and unsupported involvement in a case of MSBP abuse.

Re-asserting old recommendations from inquiry reports

The child death inquiries of the mid-eighties, particularly those into the deaths of Jasmine Beckford (1985), Tyra Henry (1987) and Kimberley Carlile (1987), emphasised the failings of practitioners and managers and saw some of this practice as 'dangerous'. These issues have been covered in more depth by Horwath and Kessel in Chapter 5. We wish here to re-emphasise the importance of understanding and addressing these issues in dealing with MSBP abuse.

Department of Health legislation and guidance have ensured that many of the lessons learnt from child death inquiries have been incorporated into child protection practice. The Children Act 1989 and *Working Together Under the Children Act* have resulted in improvements within inter-agency child protection practice which should be used in suspected cases of MSBP. Within this book are examples of ways in which this guidance has been effectively developed into local protocols for inter-agency working in suspected cases of MSBP.

The emphasis on parental responsibility and the move towards working in partnership with parents, has resulted in a re-examination of practice, particularly around the value of involving parents in investigation and assessment. This is challenging work, but in cases of MSBP may be impossible to achieve. We have already outlined our concerns with regard to partnership in the introduction and would like to restate the central dilemma here. How can one work in partnership with those who are deliberately subverting professional trust in order to continue significantly harming their children? We need to keep this in mind and not give away our vested authority to protect children in order to uphold an ideal.

Challenging current practice

It seems to us that MSBP abuse raises five main challenges to current practice. First, paediatricians and the investigating authorities need to be working together earlier in the process if children are to be adequately protected. Second, we need to acknowledge that while covert video surveillance (CVS) is a legitimate technique for gathering information in order to protect children, everything that can be done up to and including overt surveillance, should be considered within the context of a properly constituted inter-agency forum, the strategy meeting, before the decision to use it is taken. Third, when a decision is taken to use CVS then it is our view, in accordance with John Fox, that this should be undertaken directly by the police or under police supervision. This is because CVS is being used at this point to gather evidence in relation to a serious crime: attempted murder. Fourth, we need to accept and to act on the fact that in some cases the doctor is the inadvertent but actual perpetrator of the abuse, through the imposition of unnecessary, invasive and harmful medical procedures and tests. More support and training may be required for doctors to address this sensitive issue. Finally, consideration needs to be given to the appropriate use of expert witnesses in MSBP cases, as has been argued by Terence Stephenson in Chapter 10.

Linking practice developments

It seems to us that there is much that can be learned in relation to MSBP abuse perpetrators from practice experience and literature relating to dangerousness in general and sex offenders in particular, as argued in Chapter 12 on probation work.

Some of the case examples cited within this book emphasise the way perpetrators of MSBP target and groom key personnel, who are often in powerful positions. There may be lessons relevant to MSBP that can be learnt from the work on this.

Schreier and Libow (1993) note:

> 'Her attitude reminded me of men involved in sexual offences. They use denial and always represent themselves as the victim. Sometimes they have been victimised as children, but it is still a diversion away from their own responsibility.' (p. 154)

Those who wish to explore issues of sexual offending further are referred to the recent collection edited by Morrison, Erooga and Beckett (1994).

There is a growing understanding of the importance of dissociation as a defence against trauma and of the links between this mechanism and the actions of both victims and perpetrators, both during the abuse and in disclosing it or being confronted about it. Norma Howes has addressed some of these issues in Chapter 13 and Schreier and Libow (1993) also refer to the likelihood of dissociative processes being at work.

Developing practice

There are a number of ways in which practice could be developed. Perhaps the most important of these is through the provision of training. Again, as Birchall and Hallett (1995) argue, while multiagency coordination in practice is well developed, multiagency training is not. A multiagency strategy for training in MSBP would appear to us to be crucial to a successful and effective outcome. Generally those with most responsibility for child protection work still have little or no training in discharging those responsibilities either at pre- or post-qualifying level. The training base that has been built up over recent years through the training support programme is being eroded. Much could be done both to protect children and to uphold family life by implementing an

ACPC-coordinated training programme in MSBP abuse, as we argued in the last chapter.

Second, guidance is badly needed on the issue of MSBP. This book has illustrated how complex the issues are in balancing the protection of the child with upholding family life and working in partnership. However, *Working Together* (Department of Health, 1991) has nothing explicit to say about MSBP apart from including it specifically as a form of physical abuse of children. *The Challenge of Partnership in Child Protection* (Department of Health, 1995a) asserts only that where MSBP is suspected families should not be involved until 'there is sufficient evidence to ensure the adequate protection of the child' (p43). *Medical Responsibilities* (Department of Health, 1995b) is silent on this issue. Yet it is our experience that practitioners are desperately struggling to resolve major dilemmas in a crucial arena where the management of partnership issues can literally be a life or death matter; largely without assistance. From our conversations with practitioners we feel that some specific guidance is urgently required, particularly with regard to partnership, child protection and family-centred care on children's hospital wards.

Gray, Bentovim and Milla in Chapter 11 point the way forward with regard to treatment and rehabilitation for perpetrators and this work needs to be built upon and more widely disseminated. Similarly we were encouraged to speak to a number of therapists working in isolation with adult survivors of MSBP. A forum to share this practice experience would also be a useful development.

Trust restored: developing an aware culture

In the introduction we acknowledged the current crisis in child care brought about by professionals listening to children and taking seriously their abuse by trusted adults, often in the caring profession. In our view this has presented us both individually and as a culture with a crisis over the provision of a safe environment for our children, particularly as we are all too aware through the media of the crimes of Beverley Allitt and of Jason Dabbs, a student nursery nurse convicted of sexually abusing children in his care.

It can seem that we have only one choice, when faced with the reality that people deliberately gain access to children to cause them significant harm, and that is to trust no one. We know that paedophiles can be very seductive and believable in their relations with adults and that adults can themselves be targeted for a grooming process to enable perpetrators to get access to children.

Our natural inclination is to resist bad news, and those who wish to harm children will use this to gain access to children and to keep us in collusive ignorance of their real motivation. If our trust can be abused and betrayed so calculatedly then how can we construct a basis on which to maintain trusting relationships? How can we live with the reality that individuals enter child care services with a motivation to abuse children? What can be done to try and ensure that these children are protected? What might these developments have to say about MSBP abuse?

One way out of this difficulty with trust is to seek to develop within the workplace what the Faithful Foundation have termed an 'aware culture'.

There are two main aspects to an aware culture: one attitudinal and the other environmental. For a workplace to be able to deal with abusers who mask their behaviour behind an apparently acceptable and believable facade (which would include mothers who inflict MSBP abuse on their children), then that workplace must be able first to accept that this is a possibility. A workplace that accepts everything at face value will leave children vulnerable. Equally a workplace that feels obliged to suspect the motives of every individual action will soon be unable to function.

In order to strike some form of balance between these two positions, we need to be able to put in place what Jenni Whitehead, a child protection trainer in Bradford, calls the possibility of a 'credibility gap' in our perception: an ability to compare what people say and assert with how they actually behave. This idea of a 'credibility gap' involves trust but it also means taking seriously either observed contradictions in behaviour or the doubts and concerns of others. So rather than dismissing suspicious behaviour, it should be taken seriously and people should be asked why they have behaved in that way. To quote Terence Stephenson from Chapter 1:

'Believe what you see rather than see what you believe.'

Having a basic trust of people but retaining a credibility gap will be greatly assisted by working towards providing a safe environment. This involves thinking actively about ways in which children could be abused by potential perpetrators and what can be done to minimise this. For example, the practice of giving mothers unsupervised care of their children is an important one. However, when dealing with a suspected case of MSBP then it might be important to reassess this practice in order to promote a safer environment for the child.

If we are going to seek to provide safe environments for children we must recognise that this is not an either/or situation. It is a balancing act and risk cannot be excluded totally from the equation without unacceptable limits and processes being applied to the majority. The most obvious example of this was the call, in some quarters, for the provision of security guards in maternity wards and the restriction of visiting hours following the abductions of two babies from different maternity units.

Having an aware culture in place will do much to alert us to, and to assist us to take seriously, early signs that things are not as they appear. However, it does not help us with the difficult dilemmas we face when considering the threshold at which active intervention should take place. We are well aware of the risks and the crisis that accompany a decision to act on suspicions of child abuse.

The problem is that the proof required under law may not be obtainable, so that we end up unable formally to offer protection to children about whom we have very grave concerns. This means that not only do we have to be able to accept that someone is doing harm to children, we also have to live with that long enough to have a reasonable chance of protecting the child. At this point we have to live with the knowledge that this might fail. A procedure such as CVS may be the only opportunity to get conclusive evidence with which to protect a child.

These dilemmas are difficult and acute but in MSBP abuse we are faced with them and challenged to respond sensitively on behalf of the child. We should respond to family members with sensitivity but our working culture should be aware of and alert to suspicions of abuse and able to respond sensitively when things are not what they seem. This practice needs to be extended to the people we work with as well as the families in our care.

Further exploration

Central issues of race and gender in MSBP abuse have been acknowledged but not directly addressed in this book. This was not through lack of effort on our part. We failed to find anyone who had worked with a black family in relation to MSBP. This issue needs further exploration. While it may be possible that the pervasive influence of racism and different cultural traditions may mitigate against black mothers investing so heavily in largely white male doctors, this is unlikely to be the whole story.

The situation is slightly different with regard to gender. We have come across people who have worked with male perpetrators and some of their work is in this book. Through conversations we have also speculated about some other reasons why men might be under-represented in the figures. Are male MSBP perpetrators missed? Their violence towards children may not be assessed in the same way or given the same meaning. It may be subsumed under the category of physical abuse and the motivation may be missed. We have presumptions about men being aggressive and confrontational and women being manipulative or passive. Is this the case, in terms of perpetrating abuse, or do we as professionals assess cases in this way because of our own prejudices? This led us to think again about a neglected area of concern in relation to child deaths by the child protection system: that of men who kill their children and then commit suicide themselves. In this an aggressive by proxy form of abuse? The theme of suicide by proxy is receiving, at the time of writing, a lot of media attention via the case of Susan Smith in Union, South Carolina. Suicide by proxy is being put forward as one explanation as to why she killed her two young children by driving them into a lake.

Moving on from Munchausen syndrome by proxy?

Much has already been said both in this collection and more widely about the use of the term Munchausen syndrome by proxy. We have chosen to focus on a definition that describes the abusive behavioural aspect; others have referred to this as induced illness in children. There is little agreement about the usefulness of the term as a causal explanation of the abusive behaviour that defines a discrete psychological disorder or mental illness; indeed much of the testimony of expert witnesses in court revolves around this issue. Whether there is agreement about this or not, it still seems likely that convicted perpetrators will be contextualised as in need of 'treatment', and we have seen from Norma Howes chapter some of the forgiveness that survivors can show to perpetrators if their abuse is understood in terms of an illness.

This debate will doubtless continue to unfold as awareness grows. This book mirrors the debate at the time it was put together. It is clear to us, and to most others working directly in the field, that this current state of affairs is unsatisfactory. One of our regrets is that we were not able to include a chapter on this issue in the collection. We are, however, aware of material which should be published shortly after this book that may help to further the debate.

Finally

Through this book, we hope that we have been able to raise

practitioners' awareness of some of the issues they are likely to encounter in suspected cases of MSBP and given them a framework for making assessments. Our aim has been to move practice on, to avoid the situations described by one practitioner:

'There seems to have developed some kind of no-go area around MSBP – a dirty word which experienced professionals will not contemplate, in spite of the obviousness of it all to an outsider. I kept thinking what was wrong with me, my personality, my ability as a social worker, that only I seemed able to see what was going on? For a while I doubted my own skills and experience, leaving me rudderless, such was the force of the mother's personality and manipulation. I felt isolated, frustrated and powerless...at the failings of a system meant to protect children.'

References

Birchall, E and Hallett, C (1995) *Working Together in Child Protection.* HMSO

Department of Health (1991) *Working Together Under the Children Act 1989: a guide to arrangements for inter-agency cooperation for the protection of children from abuse.* HMSO

Department of Health (1995a) *The Challenge of Partnership in Child Protection: practice guide.* HMSO

Department of Health (1995b) *Medical Responsibilities.* HMSO

Hallett, C (1995) *Inter Agency Co-ordination in Child Protection.* HMSO

London Borough of Brent and Brent Health Authority (1985) *A Child in Trust: the report of the panel of inquiry into the circumstances surrounding the death of Jasmine Beckford*

London Borough of Greenwich and Greenwich Health Authority (1987) *A Child in Mind: protection of children in a responsible society – Report of the commission of inquiry into the circumstances surrounding the death of Kimberley Carlile*

London Borough of Lambeth (1987) *Whose Child?: the report of the panel appointed to inquire into the death of Tyra Henry*

Morrison, T, Erooga, M and Beckett, R C, (eds) (1994) *Sexual Offending against Children: assessment and treatment of male abusers.* Routledge

Schreier, H A, and Libow, J A, (1993) *Hurting for Love (Munchausen by proxy syndrome).* Guildford Press

Index

Becoming a member

The National Children's Bureau offers an extensive Library and Information Service – probably the largest child care information resource in the UK. We also run a comprehensive programme of conferences and seminars, and publish a wide range of books, leaflets and resource packs. In addition, the Bureau gives members the opportunity to tap into an influential network of professionals who care about children, helping to set the agenda for the nineties and beyond.

Membership of the National Children's Bureau provides you with:

- a quarterly mailing containing:
  - *Children UK*: the Bureau's journal
  - *Highlights:* briefing papers containing summaries of research findings and recent reports of legislation on relevant issues;
- access to the library and information service including databases, books, journals and periodicals;
- first access to the findings of our research and development projects;
- advance notice of our extensive programme of conferences and seminars throughout the country and concessionary prices;
- concessionary prices and advance details for Bureau publications.

The National Children's Bureau can support you in the day-to-day task of meeting the needs of children and young people. For further details please contact Jane Lewis, Membership Marketing Coordinator, National Children's Bureau, 8 Wakley Street, London EC1V 7QE or call 0171 843 6047 for further information.

Publications

Recent works include:

Balancing the Act

Social Work and Assessment with Adolescents

Children, Sex Education and the Law

Good Practice in Sex Education: A sourcebook for schools

Children's Rights and HIV

Managing to Change

Schools' SEN Policies Pack

Crossing the Boundaries

Growing Up

It's Your Meeting!

Intervention in the Early Years

The Bureau also publishes a quarterly journal, *Children & Society* – to subscribe please contact John Wiley & Sons, Tel: 01243 770634   Fax: 01243 770638

For further information or a catalogue please contact: Book Sales, National Children's Bureau, 8 Wakley Street, London EC1V 7QE Tel: 0171 843 6029   Fax: 0171 278 9512

Child and Family Support and Protection

A practical approach

Barbara Hearn, Practice Development Department
Published by National Children's Bureau Enterprises Ltd
March 1995, ISBN 1 874579 60 1

Too often, a family's first contact with social workers is through a child protection investigation and concern has arisen over the subsequent alienation of families from social workers. It is now recognised that child protection should form part of wider support for families where the child's welfare is the main focus.

Drawing on recent research, this report outlines the risk of polarising family support and child protection work by treating them as alternatives rather than as mutually supportive and complementary activities. It offers a definition of family support and outlines some practical ways in which local authorities can work towards achieving a balance between family support and child protection to the benefit of children and their families.

This practical report is essential reading for policy makers, managers, practitioners and anyone concerned with responding to the views expressed in the recent report *Seen But Not Heard* (Audit Commission, 1994) and the Department of Health's Sieff paper.

**£6.50 (Members) £8.00 (Non-members)
including post, packing and order processing**